D0274569

WITHDRAWN

The
MAN INSIDE
The JACKET

Compiled by:
Maia Dunphy, Ciaran Morrison,
Mick O'Hara, Rita Kirwan & Nicola Weldon

Published in 2009 by Tayto Ltd.
Limited Edition Copy

ISBN: 978-0-9563036-0-8

Author: Mr. Tayto

Mr. Tayto model rendered by
Brown Bag Films Ltd., Dublin.

Designed by Four5One Creative, Dublin.

Special thanks to Raymond Coyle and
to all in Tayto who contributed to this publication.

www.mrtayto.ie

Printed in Ireland

The MAN INSIDE The JACKET

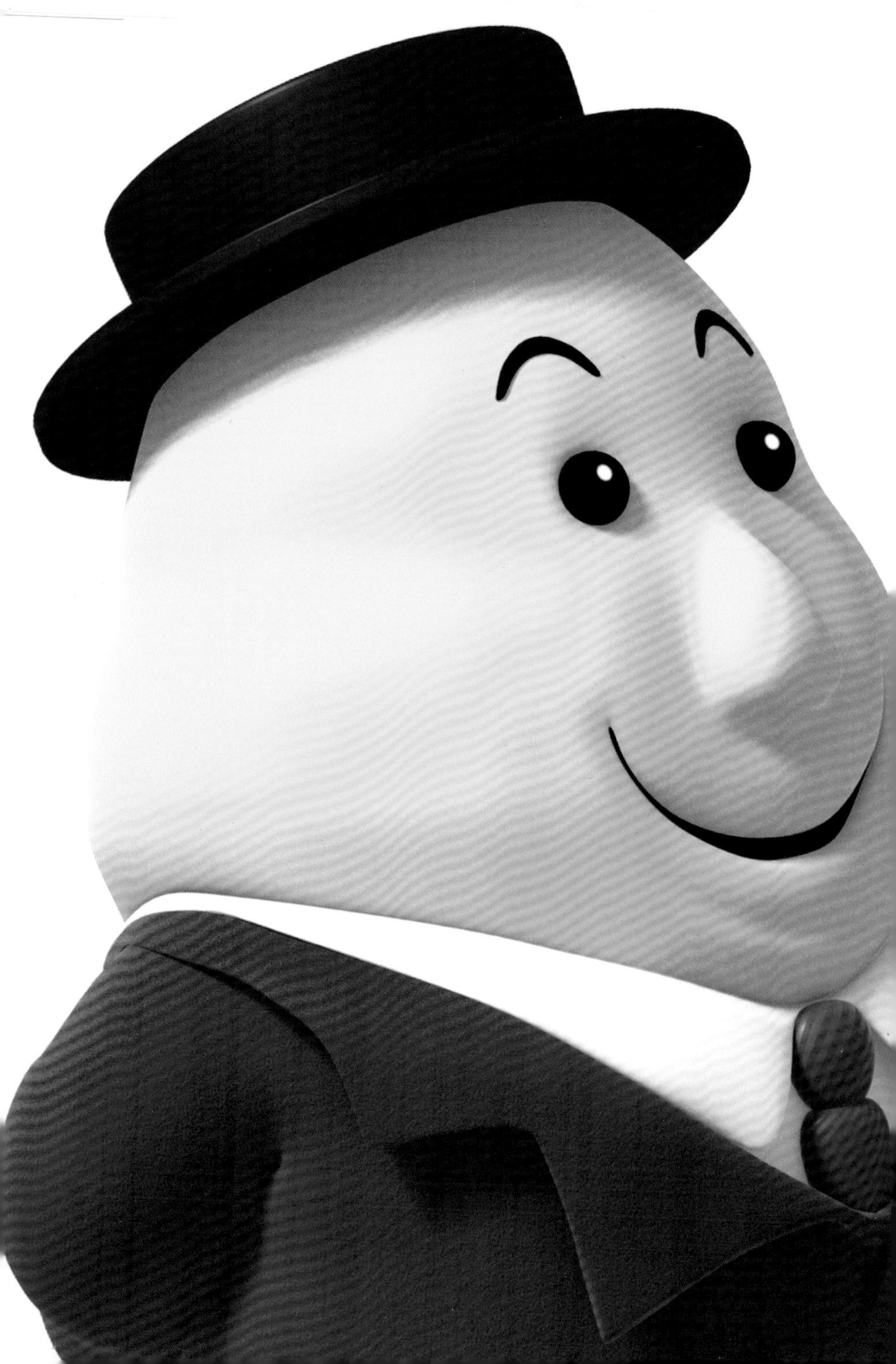

I'VE BEEN CALLED MANY THINGS IN MY YEARS ON THIS EMERALD ISLE; THICK SKINNED, THE QUIET MAN, SPUDMUFFIN, COUCH POTATO, NOT TO MENTION GIVEN A FAIR ROASTING ON MORE THAN ONE OCCASION.

So I thought it was time that I set the record straight on a few things. I'm proud of my humble roots, and how I came from Moore Street to.....well the same street really (and a second place in Meath, more of that later!). I'm the man everyone recognises, but nobody knows, but all that's about to change as I open up my life and jacket to the Irish people. A few things might surprise you – I know I look as if butter wouldn't melt, but trust me, it would.

Every Irish fella thinks they've got a book in them, but when someone told me the biggest thing the Irish abroad miss about home is Tayto Crisps I thought it's time to tell my side of the story. Everyone's got an opinion on the Big Fella in the Red Jacket and I don't want some ghost writer making up codology about me or mashing up the truth.

So here it is. My life. In these pages, I'll be baring my soul to yis all, digging up the past before anyone else does it for me. I consider myself to be a fairly streetwise spud these days; I've run for election, searched the length and breadth of this fair land for a wife and I'd like to think I'm responsible for the most famous Irish crisps in the world.

So here you are, holding my life in your hands. What you'll find wedged into these pages are bits of my childhood, pages from old diaries, letters home to Ma, and a geansaí load of other stuff that you probably never needed (or wanted!) to know.

And to those who say they've got the dirt on me, I say to the people of Ireland – never trust a potato without a bit of dirt on him!

MY FAMILY TREE

(As Far Back As Da Will Allow Me Go)

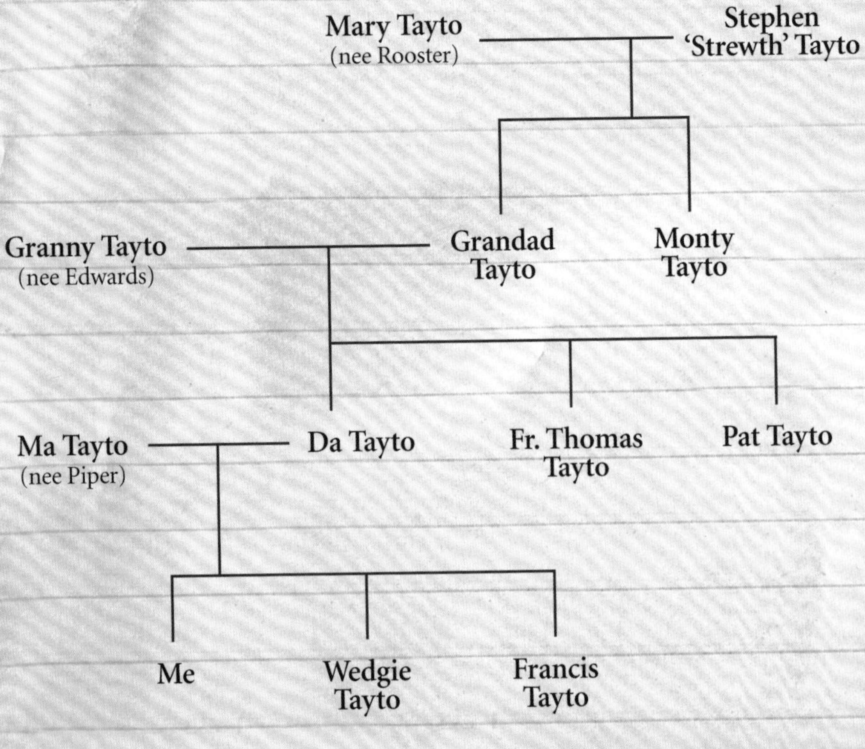

Mary Tayto (nee Rooster) — Stephen 'Strewth' Tayto

- Grandad Tayto
- Monty Tayto

Granny Tayto (nee Edwards) — Grandad Tayto

- Da Tayto
- Fr. Thomas Tayto
- Pat Tayto

Ma Tayto (nee Piper) — Da Tayto

- Me
- Wedgie Tayto
- Francis Tayto

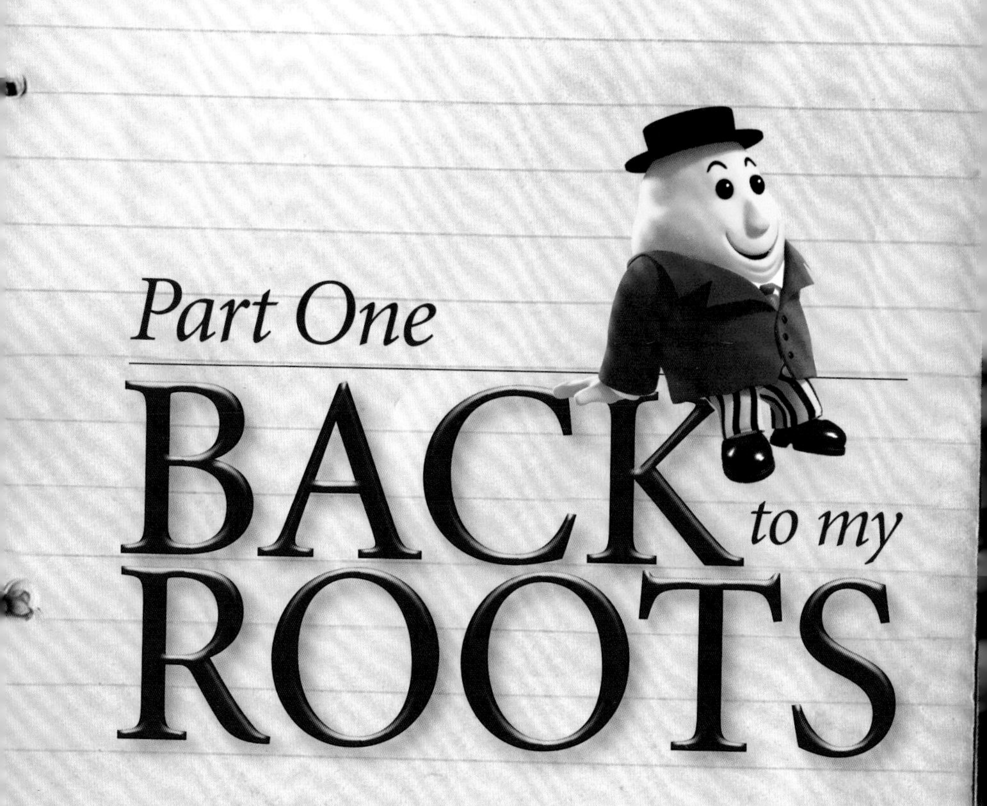

Part One BACK *to my* ROOTS

MINE WAS A HAPPY CHILDHOOD; BORN AND REARED IN DUBLIN - MOORE STREET TO BE EXACT. AT HOME IT WAS MA AND PA, GRANNY TAYTO (WHO REMEMBERS HER OWN MA TALKING ABOUT THE GREAT FAMINE - WE STILL SHUDDER AT THE THOUGHT OF IT), AND TWO BROTHERS WEDGIE AND FRANCIS AT HOME.

Tayto Crisp Bag. Circa 1955

Not a lot of people know this, as we're a pretty modest clan, but my family accidentally invented the first flavoured 'potato crisp' in 1954 when I was only a chisler. Granny Tayto used to make homemade chips three times a week, and still carrying the burden of years of hardship, the chips got thinner and thinner to save on potatoes, until eventually she was cutting them so fine she'd get twenty out of one spud! She'd still cover them in salt and vinegar like regular chips. The family used to laugh about this but we all started to really like Granny's thin, crispy potatoes. One night, Pa was going out to the pub and brought some leftover crispy potatoes in a bag to share with the boys and they went down a storm. Pretty soon, Pa and his best mate, Joe 'Spud' Murphy, were making crisps themselves every Friday afternoon to bring down the pub. I'd come in from school, and they'd have their system going - Pa slicing the potatoes by hand, Joe on frying duty and between them, they'd get a dozen bags of crisps cooked by 6 o'clock. Granny was thick with them for giving away potatoes; 'They don't grow on trees y'know boys!' she'd say. So they thought about maybe starting to charge for them. Demand for Pa and Spud's crisps soon exceeded their supply and as Pa was out of work at the time, he thought, why not give it a proper go? So they did! We'd only a small house, but a whole room had to be given up to the crisps. Unfortunately it was me and the brothers' room, as we were told Granny was too old to be giving up hers. She always said it would be soon enough we'd have our room back for good, which made us feel bad so we didn't complain (even though she secretly thought she'd outlive all of us!).

Forget the Rat Pack, here's the Multi-pack.
(L-R) Joe Spud Murphy, George Colley & Allan W Adams.

The Taoiseach Séan Lemass (far right) getting very excited to cut the ribbon and get stuck into a complimentary bag of Cheese & Onion.

So every morning, we had to fold away our beds before heading to school so Pa and Joe could set up the house-factory. Soon they needed more than just the two of them, so they recruited the very first members of the Tayto team - Seamus Burke, Ben Kealy and a mate of Ma's called Bernie Kane. It was Seamus and Spud who invented the first cheese and onion flavour! The spuds were washed in a big old bath and rolled down a tube through the slicer and into another bath. (One of them was our bath which made Ma steaming mad, but us kids were thrilled as we didn't have to use it anymore). Then they were put into packets. Bernie had incredibly steady hands, and she used to seal the bags with a bit of glue on a paintbrush to keep them from spoiling.

She used to joke to all the kids about glueing our mouths shut if she heard us cursing! We never thought she would, but it made us think twice… Soon there was a team of eight and a van making up the company and the Tayto empire was well on its way. They were a great bunch - Seamus and Bernie, Matty Duane, Joe Bunney, Paddy Lillis, Paddy Enright and Kevin Masterson. I was a real chip off the old block and learned the business of crisps at a young age - mainly because my bedroom was the first factory so I couldn't avoid it. I'm not pretending to be Bill Cullen, but you did what you had to – I imagine there's no way Bill enjoyed getting up at the crack of dawn to sell apples out of a barrow. He used to bob over from Summerhill some mornings with a big grumpy head on him. He got an idea to make penny apple crisps but they never caught on. Anyway, Pa had to drag me out of bed in the morning to help him with the deliveries, but he always said if we didn't get up, we'd risk being made into crisps ourselves!

But life was good back then. This was in a time before iPods, hoverbikes, mobile phones and when a holiday meant getting the bus to the beach and sitting in a damp caravan for a week with a pack of cards. These were the days when we spent all our time outside, played in building sites, broke bones and no one got sued. We didn't know the difference between 'good' and 'bad' fats and no one had ever heard of a disease called obesity; if a kid was fat, you just chased him till he got thin, or better still, made him be goalie. Organic food hadn't been invented, because all food was, and nobody died from drinking rain water. If you had a bike at all you were lucky and it was always a hand-me-down. You could only get strawberries in the summer and nobody washed them first. And Spam was something that only came in a tin, as Bill Gates was only in Higher Infants and hadn't come up with the idea of a computer.

In 1959 something big happened to our little company. One of the fellas who worked with me Pa called in saying his wife was doing catering for a big event and needed snacks for a smart drinks reception. As far as we were concerned, smart drinks were anything with a straw and ice in them, but we knew that our crisps would go with anything. Pa sorted her out with a load of freshly cooked Tayto and they went down a storm. Turned out it was only Eamon De Valera's inauguration! At the end of the night Dev himself requested a few bags to take home and the first ever 'six-pack' of Tayto was born. Once people found out The Long Fella himself was a fan, the nation went mad for them. Pretty soon the Tayto team needed much more space than our little house, and to be honest, none of us had had a bath in months, so they found a place suitable for a factory up in Coolock and it all took off from there.

The Smallest Tayto Shop, opened in Co. Donegal

The factory in Coolock was really something. Pa and Joe had looked around for the best location and worked out that the obvious choice was to be closer to the single most important element of Tayto - the potatoes! At that time, nearly all of the spuds came from north county Dublin, so Coolock was a perfect choice. I remember well the day it opened in 1968. George Colley, the Minister for Trade and Industry at the time did the honours, and it was the biggest day out I'd ever seen. I remember telling Minister Colley that I'd be taking over one day. He patted me on the head and said he'd look forward to coming back the day I did.

It was massive - the biggest thing we'd ever seen (although to be fair, we only had our bedroom to compare it to), and they had all sorts of machinery brought in, moving conveyor belts, bigger slicing machines and not a bathtub in sight.

Every place in the country wanted to stock Tayto, and people even started opening shops in the middle of nowhere just to sell them.

My Pa was a great old skin. I used to love driving round the country with him and Spud delivering the crisps. Pa was a great man for the stories and would be telling me all about the family history and all the Taytos around the world. I was told afterwards that only some of the stories were true, but I could never work out which ones. We were always taught in school that Walter Raleigh planted the first ever potatoes in Ireland in the 1580's. Pa said this was rubbish and he knew for a fact that it was one of the earliest recorded members of our family – Turlough O'Taytaigh – who brought spuds back from Spain at least twenty years before Wally even set one pointy shoe on Irish soil. He also said he thought it went back much further. 5000 years further to be exact, and did we think it was a coincidence that Newgrange is shaped like a potato? We went on a school trip there and do you know what? It does look like a big spud from above. As for that giant Maris Piper at the entrance!

The Irish Times Front Page Ad, 1962

The Irish Times Front Page Ad, 1963

The Irish Times Ad, 1959

The First Tayto Print Ad 1954

On the long drives across Ireland delivering Taytos, Pa would tell me about all the Taytos who'd emigrated. Before the days of Budget Travel, Ryanair, charity walks in Peru with Alan Hughes and extradition, the Irish went abroad for lots of reasons other than holidays and cheap duty free. And not just during the famine, which the family don't like to talk about for obvious reasons. There was my great uncle, Bernardo Tayto who bought a farm half the size of Ireland in Argentina for the price of a Hot Press Yearbook back in the '30s. (Bernardo started the trend of just putting an 'o' after your name to make it sound more Argentinean. Pretty soon Bernardo, Johnno, Micko, and Decko became what the Argentineans thought were traditional Irish names).

Che Guevara was forever calling into his farm looking for Taytos after he tried a bag in Hanratty's Hotel in Limerick during a Shannon stopover on the way to Cuba in 1965. Massive fan of Cheese & Onion Tayto was Che according to my Pa. When the films came out last year I was thinking of putting out a commemorative pack of 'Che & Onion' – could be a big seller down Cuba way.

There was Pat Tayto who went off to America in the '50s. He worked in a diner at first, and pretty quickly introduced crisps to New York. He explained to the rest of the staff that they had started out as Granny Tayto's thin potato 'chips', and the name stuck so they've called them Potato Chips over there ever since. They were so popular, people came from far and wide to try them and for a while, New York was known as The Big Potato before The Big Apple eclipsed it. Soon Pat had gone on to become Chief of Police of the NYPD. In fact, 'potato chips' were the favourite snack of the New York cops before some rookie in the '70s accidentally shot a hole in someone's iced bun and unwittingly invented the doughnut. Then there was Father Thomas Tayto who joined the Christian Brothers and went off to Africa.

He sent back an idea he got from one of the locals there for spicy fish curry Taytos. We never tried it but just told him we had, and then said a rake of Hail Marys to make up for the lie.

My Pa told me the Tayto clan had travelled to all four corners of the globe. We've always had the gift of the gab - floury sorts we are - and as Pa always said "Where there's a will, there's a Tayto!"

Granny Tayto's Crisp Recipes

Cheese & Onion Crisp Sandwich

A classic combo this one. If someone doesn't like this then they're weird.

Ingredients:

2 slices white sliced pan
butter
1 packet Cheese and Onion Tayto

Method:

Butter bread. Crush crisps and sprinkle onto one half of buttered bread, place second slice on top. If you want to impress a girlfriend, try using a fancy French stick.

Smokey Bacon Crisp Sandwich

The predecessor to today's BLT. The height of sophistication in crisp sandwiches.

Ingredients:

2 slices white batch
butter
1 packet smokey bacon Tayto
Lettuce and tomato (optional)

Method:

Butter batch. Scatter on crushed crisps as in previous recipe. Add lettuce and tomato if desired or if you're on a diet.

Crisp Coddle

A complicated one this. But Granny used to cook it on a Tuesday and it would last till Friday.

1 pound pork sausage
1 pound gammon
1 quart boiling water
2 large yellow onions, chopped, seasoning
3 packets Tayto Smokey Bacon Crisps

Method:

Chop the meat into 1 inch pieces. Place into boiling water and boil for 5 minutes. Cover and simmer gently for about 1 hour, or until the liquid is reduced by half and all the ingredients are cooked. Sprinkle with crushed Smokey Bacon crisps and serve with a pint. (Red Cadet for the children)

TAYTOS AROUND *the* WORLD

HERE ARE SOME OF MY MOST FAMOUS RELATIVES, WHO FOR SOME REASON MY DA COULD NEVER EXPLAIN WERE WRITTEN OUT OF THE HISTORY BOOKS.

'STREWTH' TAYTO

FR THOMAS TAYTO

MONTY TAYTO

TURLOUGH O'TAYTAIGH (b.1540 - d.1601) Cork and Spain.
Turlough had a lifelong hatred of Walter Raleigh as he brought a half-stone of spuds back from Spain 20 years before Raleigh, whilst on a spice and gun running trip in 1560.

JOSEPH TAYTO (b.1801 - d.1880) Newfoundland.
Completely unemployable in Ireland, 'Joey' heard about the cod fishing empire in Newfoundland, Canada, and thought with that much fish about the place, they'll be needing chips. Left with a few sacks of spuds and some batter and made a fortune with Joey's Fish and Chippers.

'STREWTH' TAYTO (b. 1823 - d.1871) Bannagher then Australia
Stephen Tayto was arrested in 1845 for sending rude shaped potatoes to a convent. He was shipped off to Australia a year later. Credited with coining the term 'strewth', as he regaled other cons with stories of leaving a phallic shaped spud on Sister Ruth's reading desk. 'Sister Ruth!' became a term of surprise, which was later shortened to 'strewth'.

MONTY TAYTO (b. 1895 - d.1993) Montserrat.
Unpopular in his hometown of Raphoe, Monty heard they loved the Irish in Montserrat, so emigrated in 1914. He spent a long happy life with several wives, and was the grand marshal of the Paddy's Day parade till the year he died aged 98.

FR THOMAS TAYTO (b.1922 - d.2004).
Joined the missions and went off to Africa in 1950. Credited with bringing crisps to Burkina Faso. Often used to write home with African inspired flavours, including spicy fish curry, egg and yam, but none of them caught on.

PAT TAYTO (b.1934) New York.
Pat went to America in the 50's with a head full of dreams and a pocket full of potatoes. He ended up Chief of Police of the NYPD in the seventies. He was a consultant on a famous TV show called CHIPs.

EDUCATING TAYTO

AH SCHOOL DAYS....THE HAPPIEST DAYS OF YOUR LIFE SO THEY SAY. I'D LIKE TO KNOW WHO FIRST SAID THAT, BECAUSE I DON'T KNOW ANYONE WHO REALLY THINKS IT!

School was grand, but to be honest, I just wanted to work in the factory with Pa. It always seemed like much better craic than learning about stuff from the past or algebra. Although I was pretty good at basic maths because I used to run me own tuck-shop at break time in the yard. No prizes for guessing what I was selling! I tried to keep it quiet from all the teachers, and thought I'd succeeded until some of them started asking me could they get a six-pack of Tayto off me after school. I had to give them a reduced rate though. They loved crisps those Christian Brothers! One good thing about school was that you could always twist things to suit yourself. I used to love science and spent all my free-study time in the chemistry lab. Pa was always telling me about the mad ways new flavours were discovered, so I thought I'd use my time to impress them all by doing it scientifically. Fr. Murphy the science teacher got wise to me though and I nearly failed the year because of it. I had told him I was doing a project on rainwater that would take me the whole year.

He walked in one day to find me sprinkling chilli powder onto a potato and he didn't buy my excuse that I was testing the effects of spicy rain on vegetables. To be fair to him, he let me finish the project on the condition I let him try the results. The less said about the coddle flavour the better. But he did think the tomato soup flavour was a real winner but it never caught on...mainly 'cos Pa said putting a sachet of soup into every bag would never be a runner.

But sure I was only a chisler back then, so didn't really know any better. Fr Darcy said I'd make a great priest with the dedication I showed, but once he found out about my money spinning tuck shop and my eye for the girls he didn't mention it again.

Every morning I'd meet the lads at the end of the street and we'd head into school together. Me, Coyler, Micko, Quinner and Doyler. We all lived near each other and were always getting into a bit of trouble here and there. Not serious stuff. Fr. Brendan once caught us with a packet of John Player Blue around the back of the school chapel and beat the legs off us. He sent letters home and when Coyler's Pa realised where all his fags were going, he went through the roof. My Pa was pretty calm about it. Or so I thought. I got home and he gave me a pack of cigarettes…. and then put me in the cupboard under the stairs and made me smoke all twenty back to back. I was sick as a dog! Never smoked again after that though!

1.Wedgie 2.Francis 3.Doyler 4.Coyler 5.Micko 6.Quinner 7.Meself

I had two younger brothers - Wedgie who was two years younger than me and Francis who was four. So I had to bring them along to school with me when they started. Wedgie always wanted to be hanging around with my mates, and we put up with him most of the time. Francis was always a bit of a couch potato and even when he grew up, was always more into the books and staying in than cramping my style. But they were always decent skins my two brothers.

The lads used to be always slagging me because I used to have to wear my own clothes to school – there was a uniform of sorts, but I couldn't get one to fit me. It would be fair to say I was a broad lad. Those were the days when you wore short trousers until your parents decided you were grown up enough for long ones, so me Ma made my trousers long so I could roll them down when the other lads in class got new ones. She was a dab hand at the sewing me Ma. Me and my brothers were the only fellas on the road who were always in jackets. In fact, us Taytos were hardly ever seen out of them! Dead smart we were.

ANNUAL SCHOOL REPORT
Name: Tayto
Class: 4B
Date: 20th June 1969

HISTORY - C+: Tayto is a spirited youngster but often seems
misinformed. In his last exam he wrote about Newgrange being
the oldest monument in the world dedicated to potatoes. Very
convincing argument but he needs to read the text books provided.

MATHS - C: Tayto doesn't really apply himself in class which
is shame, as he seems to be quite the human calculator at break
times, when he's selling bags of crisps in the yard.

GEOGRAPHY - B: Very knowledgeable student. Knows facts about
nearly every country in the world. He says he sees Geography
class as one big travel agency but it's still great to see a pupil
reading outside the course. This boy will travel.

SCIENCE - C: this young man should be getting an F by rights.
Said he was working on a yearlong project for his exams. We
trusted him, and then discovered he was using the chemistry lab
to create new crisp flavours. The only reason we're passing him is
because the tomato soup flavour was surprisingly tasty.

PE - B+: Enthusiastic team player. Loves the football. His unusual
build means he's mainly in goals, but when he does get a chance to
play midfield, he does well - you'd swear he had eyes in the back
of his head.

OVERALL COMMENTS: Tayto is an enthusiastic pupil. Occasionally
he does come out with some half-baked ideas, but he's fairly
thick-skinned and has a way of buttering up his teachers. He says
he doesn't want to stay on to do his Leaving Cert, but we'll keep
chipping away at him as we'd very much like to see him next year.

Back of the net? Not on my watch!

I remember going to a Formal down the social club and all the lads knocking on the door asking Ma could they borrow a jacket off one of us. I said we should rent them out but Ma said we couldn't be making money off friends and neighbours. So I just got the lads to pay me outside the house for them. A shilling apiece.

One thing school was great for was the sport – I loved the GAA and still do. We'd a great football team. The only problem was, I was always stuck in goal. The lads told me it was because I was the best goalie they'd ever seen. I was chuffed to bits until me brother pointed out it was probably more to do with the fact that I was twice as wide as everyone else. Still, it's good to know your strengths Pa always said! Played a bit of soccer too. Me and the lads used to mark out the pitch and goalposts on the street with potatoes which drove Granny mad!

She'd come storming out when we were called in for our tea, giving out yards as she picked them all up. Again, I was usually in goal, but the odd time I was up at midfield, they said I played as if I had eyes in the back of me head. I remember meeting future Irish manager Brian Kerr once.

Our club were playing Crumlin United away and I was told I couldn't wear me usual goalie shorts because their keeper Kerr had the same colour. So I asked Ma to run me up some new ones at short notice and on the day she only goes and hands me a pair of pink ones. Turns out the only material she had lying about was an old dress of hers. I was mortified, but had to wear them for all our away matches after that as Ma refused to make me any more till I had grown out of them. Got myself the nickname Kerr's Pink for that one which stuck for a lot longer than I'd have liked.

Me and the lads liked school as much as you could, but back then it was all about getting out to work. We spent our summers working in the factory - mainly sorting spuds - but it gave us all a bit of a buzz for earning money. Those summers were great. Long evenings and always sunny. We'd bring crisps back from the factory and bribe the girls for a kiss with them down by the river. One girl Kitty Murphy would kiss you on the lips for a six-pack. There was always a lovely taste of cheese and onion off her. After a couple of summers of that she was the size of a house. Quinner ended up marrying her years later so we were banned from ever talking about the "crisps for kisses" years! She still loves seeing me come up the drive on December 24th with the big Christmas box of Tayto though!

We all left school in 1970, except for Micko who went off to a seminary as his Ma wanted him to become a priest. There were loads of priests in his family. He nearly did too, studied and did the whole works. Lasted a couple of years before the priests realised he was never going to be able to give up girls! Even the nuns loved him. He went into teaching in the end so all that extra learning didn't go to waste. But that first summer after school finished, we went on our first holiday on our own. I couldn't believe it when Ma said I could go (only she made me take my younger brother Wedgie with me). Even Micko was allowed come. So we took our savings from working in the factory, packed a tent and a load of crisps and headed for the bright lights of Bettystown. It was great to be out of school and let loose on the world!

15th June 1970

Can't believe Ma let us come to Bettystown on our own this year for the holliers. I had me speech about being nearly 16 all ready, but I think in the end she just wanted a bit of peace and quiet. She made me bring me little brother Wedgie though which is a pain in the swiss, but it was that or not go at all. So me, him, Coyler, Quinner, Doyler and Micko, got the bus up to Laytown yesterday morning. Micko's Ma packed us sandwiches only they were fish paste so the driver said either they leave the bus or we do, so we chucked them out the window. Doyler hid one under the seat so that'll teach that driver next time. We got there before dinnertime and pitched our tents on the beach, well the one tent and a tarpaulin off Quinner's Da so we'll take it in turns. Saw a load of girls around which is grand as long as we can shake off the little Wedgie.

16th June 1970

Feckin' Coyler can't pitch a tent to save his life. Woke up with the tent floating in the sea this morning. Still the sun came out, so I peeled off me jacket, rubbed on a bit of sun flower oil and roasted for a few hours, whilst keeping one eye on the ladies of course! Quinner found a fiver in the sand which we spent on smokes and a flagon. Then we went swimming. Inspired by me they all put a potato down their jocks to make our packets look bigger and impress the girls who kept walking by us on the beach. Unfortunately the girls nearly wet themselves laughing at Quinner. We had to tell him you're supposed to put it down the front. Eejit. Still, at least it broke the ice with the girls, who said we could meet them later at the bumpers.

17th June 1970

We've run out of money, trying to impress the girls, buying them candy floss and goes on the bumpers, so we hatched a magic plan today to break into the amusements tonight after they close, we can't afford to go otherwise. We're going to tell the girls we opened it especially for them. We've got it all planned and sure what could go wrong?

An Garda Síochána
Laytown, Co. Meath

CASE NUMBER: BTSY3567

INCIDENT: Break in at Bettystown Amusements

REPORTING OFFICER: Thomas Whelan
DATE OF REPORT: 17th June 1970

Gardai were called to the amusements at Bettystown after a local reported a group of youths might have broken in. When we arrived, we only found one well built fella who had been tied to the Laughing Policeman and appeared to be crying. Name logged as Tayto, had nothing on him but a return bus ticket to Dublin and a potato down the front of his trousers. No damage done. Warning issued without charge.

DECK *the* HALLS *with* BAGS *of* TAYTO

CHRISTMAS WHEN I WAS A KID WAS MAGICAL. THESE WERE BACK IN THE DAYS WHEN CHRISTMAS DIDN'T START IN AUGUST, NO ONE QUESTIONED WHY SANTY DIDN'T BRING EVERYTHING ON YOUR LIST, AND A TANGERINE WAS CONSIDERED A DECENT STOCKING FILLER.

The only thing that happened early back in those days was the Christmas cake. We all knew when Ma would come home some time in November laden down with bags of dried fruit that Christmas was about six weeks away. We'd be counting the days as she took the cake out once a week and poured whiskey over it. Jaysus, you'd get drunk on the smell of one of Ma's Christmas cakes. Pa used to say there was so much booze in it, it'd never go off. Me and the brothers decided to put this to the test one year and hid a slice behind the sideboard on Stephen's Day. Of course we forgot about it. The long and the short of it is, it did go off eventually which is how it was found, so don't try that one at home (unless you like mice and a clip around the ear).

The 8th of December was always, and still is, a big day in Dublin when all the culchies take the day off to come up to the big smoke to do their shopping. Most Dubliners just stay in on the 8th unless they're selling stuff, as the whole city does be jammed. Pa and Joe used to set up a crisp stall on Moore Street, and they'd make a killing on the 8th. One year their second customer of the day cleaned them out, saying she wanted enough Tayto to last till January, and that's when they got the idea of doing big Christmas boxes of Tayto - they were easier to stack and harder to nick! People went mad for them and it's still a real Irish tradition to pick up a big auld box of crisps to keep in the house in December. I think it's the main reason I still get asked to so many Christmas do's....

Back then, Christmas didn't really start till the 23rd, and that's when we'd all go out with Pa, get a tree and a load of stuff to decorate the house. Granny Tayto loved making arrangements, but wasn't very good at it. She once tried to make a crib for outside the house out of holly and it scratched the hands off every kid in the street, so Pa said she had to keep her decorations inside from then on. Christmas Eve we'd light a candle in the window and all head off to Midnight Mass.

We were all so excited to be up so late and wondering why the church smelled like Ma's Christmas cake. When we got home, we'd leave out a bottle of Guinness and a packet of cheese and onion for Santy before being sent to bed giddy as goats. To this day the smell of the turkey stuffing and boiled ham brings me right back to those glorious days. On Christmas morning, we were always told we weren't allowed get up before 7, so we'd wait till we heard Gran's old clock striking the hour before we'd leg it downstairs to see what was under the tree.

Those were the days when you couldn't just nip to a local garage or Spar on Christmas Day to pick up a pint of milk. Everywhere was closed - sure even the internet would have been closed on Christmas Day back then if it had been invented yet - and no one forgot to buy batteries, as none of our presents needed them. It took us years to work out that the

TAYTO
The Original Crisp
CHEESE & ONION
CHRISTMAS PACK
20 packets of Cheese & Onion
TAYTO
The Original Crisp
CHRISTMAS
VARIETY PACK
20
TAYTO
CHRISTMAS
VARIETY PACK

bike Francis got one year had been Wedgie's two years before, and mine two years before that, clever ould Santa had resprayed it and wrapped it back up! Now that's the ultimate in recycling!

I remember one year in 1968 when the whole street had a power cut on the night of the 24th and everyone thought Christmas would be cancelled. But Pa and Joe had the idea to open up the new factory and take everyone up there. So there were about 150 of us all sitting around singing carols, eating crisps and turkey sandwiches washed down with bottles of Guinness and Red Lemonade. Pa even turned on the machines and we all made our own crisps and everyone took a box home. There was a bit of a debate about what the best flavour was, so Pa said they could mix them up. And presto! The variety Christmas box was born! At about midnight the guards turned up after someone said he thought the place was being robbed. I don't think the guards got home till sometime on the 27th. Say what you like but the Irish know how to throw a party!

Q: What kind of crisps do men who are waiting to have their haircut like?
A: Barber-queue
Q: What kind of crisps do skangers like?
A: Assault 'n' vinegar
Q: What do you say to an angry 400lb spud?
A: Anything, just to butter him up.
Q: What's a frogs favourite crisp?
A: Croaky Bacon
Q: What's Posh Spice's favourite flavour?
A: Smokey Beckham
Q: What's a chiropodists favourite crisp?
A: Cheese and Bunion!

TAYTO *is* ANIM DOM!

THE SUMMER AFTER OUR FIRST TRIP ON OUR OWN TO BETTYSTOWN, WE HAD HIGH HOPES FOR MAYBE BEING ALLOWED GET THE BOAT TO ENGLAND FOR A HOLIDAY.

But Ma was having none of it. She said that this year I had to buckle down as the Inter Cert was less than a year away and I needed some help. I couldn't believe it – Fr. Dunphy had written home telling them that Irish was letting me down and it might be an idea to think about shipping me off to the Gaeltacht. I told Ma I would think about it, and I did, and that the answer was "No bleedin way", but she'd only gone and enrolled me already and paid the deposit. And we all know, once your Ma's handed over money for something, there's no going back. I went out to meet the lads to tell them our planned summer was ruined, and when I saw the long faces I realised Fr. Dunphy had sent the same letter to nearly all of them except Micko. But he said he may as well come too if we were all going. Playing 'three and in' on your own for the entire summer would drive him mental. We thought Fr. Dunphy must have been getting backhanders from some Gaeltacht college as Quinner's Irish was pretty good. Only Doyler got off as he had to go and work on his Uncle's farm in New Ross that year, on account of him having a broken leg after a cow sat on him. But we thought we may as well make the best of it – we were all going to the same place, a college in Carraroe, so we thought it'd be like a holiday of sorts. And we had the most important Irish word of all in our heads – cailiní!

Only when we got there did we realise it wasn't going to be any sort of a holiday at all, and you couldn't even choose who you lived with. Coyler ended up in a house with three poncey southsiders, Micko was on his own with a mad old crone of a Bean an Tí and Quinner was in a room share with one other fella from Cavan, who ya couldn't get a word out of when he was awake, but shouted and walked and even sang in his sleep. Quinner reckoned the lack of sleep that summer caused his growth to be stunted. (But my Pa said he was always going to be a short arse, you could tell by looking at his Da). And then there was me. I was the last to get off the bus at the end of the town, and my Bean an Tí was waiting at the door for me. She seemed nice enough, and things were grand for the first day. Up until it was time to eat. After that summer I will never take decent home cooking for granted again. Breakfast was porridge, which she'd make once a week and pour into a wooden drawer so you'd have to cut a slice out every morning, but by day three it was like trying to eat tarmac. Then at tea time we had the only thing she knew how to cook; boiled up vegetables. Monday was cabbage soup, Tuesday beans, Wednesday potato, Thursday cauliflower and the other days was a combination of all of them. Except for Fridays when she had fish. And you haven't lived till you've tried boiled cod. I didn't eat any meat at all that summer and wrote home to Ma asking her to send something. She said she was sure it wasn't that bad and it'd make me appreciate her cooking when I got home. But it was that bad as the Bean an Tí's own son lived in the house and he was white as a ghost and Micko reckoned he had rickets. At least Ma sent me a couple of boxes of Tayto though, but I barely got a packet myself as they were like gold-dust to our dried-out taste buds!

The days were spent going to classes, looking at girls, doing organised activities, looking at girls, going to Ceilís in the evening and looking at girls. Unfortunately the two big 'no, nos' in the Gaeltacht were also the two most tempting; speaking English and getting off with a girl. Both would get you sent home if you were caught. So we all decided to wait until the Céilí Mor at the end of the summer before we made our moves on the ladies. And besides I was too hungry most of the time to think of romance at all.

The sports there were alright and we were allowed take boats out together and there were plenty of football matches and the like, and I wasn't always put in goal which made a change! We all thought each of us had the worst accommodation but by the end, we all agreed Micko probably had it the worst. He was all on his own with his Bean an Tí except for her 11 cats and he said she had a couple of really long hairs coming out of her chin which he was sure he saw touching off his scramble eggs in the morning. I said I'd have put up with that just to have some eggs, but thinking back, I'm not sure I would. Coyler may have been stuck with ponces, but we think he liked it, as we know for a fact he still keeps in touch with those lads today. They do a four ball and drinks every Christmas in some posh golf club, but he always tells us he's visiting some old Auntie or something. Anyway the Fear an Tí in his gaff ran a butchers' so he had meat every other day. He snuck us in a few sausages one day and they were the best sausages I'd ever tasted. To be fair, I'd had nothing but soup for a month. I was a bleedin' wind machine!

So the Ceilí Mor was fast approaching and after making eyes at our favourite cailiní for weeks, we were all gearing up for our last chance of a bit of summer romance.

They were a bit strict over there about drinking and smoking and the like, so we had to think of a way to make it a good night without getting into trouble. Quinner said he seen his older brother making Poitín and he was sure he knew how to do it. A week before the ceilí, we all met at Micko's gaff as we reckoned his Bean an Tí was the least likely to notice. I'd brought the potatoes and Micko found yeast in the cupboard in the cat woman's kitchen. Quinner showed us how to put it all together and we left it to ferment out the back. It was going to be a night to remember. The day arrived and Micko turned up with our home brew in a couple of jars. Quinner reckoned it shouldn't have looked the way it did but we thought we'd give it a go after all the effort we'd gone to.

That was our first mistake, the second was going to the Ceilí after drinking the concoction.

I have a vague memory of girls looking on in horror whilst I danced a reel in only my jocks, I remember Micko spinning Miss O'Doulagh - the eighty year-old battle axe around - with his hand clamped firmly on her arse, Quinner throwing up in his shoe and then the Gardaí arriving.

Next thing I remember was the train pulling into Heuston station and the stoney faces on all our Mas'. The subject of the Gaeltacht was never raised again on our road, but the maddest thing of all was every one of us passed our Irish exams the following year.

Dear Wedgie,

Will you thank Mam for the box of Tayto, can you ask her to send some smokey bacon this week as a fella said he'd swap me a ham sandwich for a few packs. Food here is awful, all I'm eating is veg soup and my guts are in ribbons. Tell Mam I'll never complain about her food again. We've got a big céilí in a fortnight so we're making our own Poitin for it but don't tell anyone. There's a few fine cailins here so I'd say it's gonna be a big night!

See ya later Wedge! Hi to everyone.
T

Wedgie Tayto
Coolock
Dublin 5

TEENAGE CHIPS

BECAUSE I'M SUCH A SHARP DRESSER WITH MY TRADEMARK RED SUIT, CRISP WHITE SHIRT, BLUE TIE, PIN STRIPE TROUSERS AND TRADEMARK HAT MOST PEOPLE NEVER CONSIDER THAT AT ONE TIME I WAS A TEENAGER TOO.

The Seventies in Dublin belonged to me and the lads. It was a lot grimmer back then, we didn't have half the stuff and facilities that teens have nowadays. Bad teeth, bad skin and bad haircuts were par for the course for all teenagers. But it didn't mean you couldn't have the craic! I remember hopping on the bus, dodging the conductor and before you knew it you could be in the city centre mooching around, larking about and making a menace of yourself.

Of course top of the teen agenda was sniffing after girls, and foreign ones were the Holy Grail. I mean back in the seventies, Dublin wasn't all cosmopolitan and multi-ethnic like it is now. It's hard to believe, but to see a Spanish au pair back then was like casting your eyes on Venus herself. And if you managed to get off with one, you were a 'legend'. And so for many summers in my teenage years I was dreaming, like all fellas, of finding my own exotic foreign girl, with a sexy accent, sallow skin and all sophisticated with her fancy cigarettes and espresso coffee. I can't remember who came up with it, but the best trick to meet a foreign filly was to go to the trad bars in town. Now obviously you had to put up with a load of ould codgers fiddle playing and bashing bodhrans, but this is where the French and German girl tourists would come in search of a 'real' taste of Ireland.

Whilst Doyler and Coyler were attempting to overcome the language barrier with twin Frauleins from Hamburg, I was thinking to myself about inventing the Tayto 'Pub Crisp' range so that all the tourists could enjoy the craic agus ceol along with a 'real cheese & onion' taste of Ireland.

Of course beggars can't be choosers, and there were hardly enough foreign girls to go around all of us, so we'd always end up trying our luck a little closer to home. But of course looking back on it, the real reason we tried our luck with the foreigners was that the local girls could see right through us. I suppose we were awful eejits really, considering how gorgeous most Irish girls are!

Now if you were lucky enough to hook up with a girl in the seventies, Irish or otherwise, then there were only two entertainment options. Nobody brought girls out for meals or took them on fancy weekend breaks to Spas. No, there was the cinema or the dancing! Mind you, you had to choose your pictures well, I was dating this lovely nurse from Kildare one summer when I mistakenly took her to The Godfather and her being a horse lover legged it out of the place when the horse's head appeared in the bed! Worse still was the barmaid I took to The Exorcist. Remember the head spinning sequence? Well, it nearly scared the skin off me and there's no more of a turn off for a girl than a fella cowering behind a chair whilst she laughs it off.

I didn't fare too much better at the dancing as I'm all feet, always will be. All fellas can rock out, but anything slower tempo and feet would inevitably be stood on. Mind you for a short period, disco saved us bad dancers as most of the moves involved spinning and using your arms to point either at the floor or the ceiling.

Yes, I did have to stand on someone's shoulders; actually, two people's.

The only option other than the cinema or the dancing when dating was going for a walk. Now most lads dreaded the walk as this is where the girls would usually discover that boys are indeed from Mars and you've nothing in common whatsoever. For me though, I liked the walking; I have many fond memories of trips to the zoo and strolls down Dollymount as I regaled my date with an in depth history of the potato and the precise details of the crisp making process. It's funny looking back, but Coyler and Doyler, who haven't a word to say between them had a lot more luck with the ladies!

Other than girls, a teen boy's second favourite pastime was music. Quinner was the only one with a radiogram, which was the iPod of its day. It had a radio which you could get Radio Luxemburg on and a record player that played 45's, 33's and 78's (for his Mam). We'd be wearing out the needles blasting out Thin Lizzy, The Who, Horslips and Van the Man. We were all into the rock music back then and we crammed in as many concerts as we could afford.

Other stuff I got up to was fishing. It was hard to beat a trek with the lads over to Howth for a day out on the sea. Of course this was before Dublin Bay had the traffic it does now, Coyler's uncle had a rowing boat with a little outboard on it and we'd often venture out into Dublin Bay in search of the mackerel running. But it was more about the craic than the fishing, although it did get competitive upon occasion! If one of the lads started hauling them in then the rest of us started taking it seriously. Bets would be placed, and I remember one July we spent the whole day fishing, and by the time we were rowing back in the boat it nearly went under with the weight of the fish! And I got so sunburnt that the skin nearly peeled off me! We actually made a few bob over the years selling what we'd caught back in the harbour, and always brought a few home for Mam to gut (well, I wasn't going to do it!) and fry up for tea. She had a great trick of serving the fish up on top of a big pile of buttery mash potatoes. Even a pernickety little spud like my brother Francis, who normally wouldn't touch fish, would lick his plate clean.

Before Xboxes, PS3s and the Internet, we teenagers played sport, anything from kicking a ball around the street, going to matches and playing five-a-side, or any-a-side on a sunny evening on the green. The only time we looked at a screen at home as a teenager was to watch Top of the Pops, or Grange Hill. I remember trying to persuade Pa to do a Kung Fu crisp in honour of my favourite TV series, but the idea of Sweet n' Sour flavour was way too exotic at the time, as this was well before we had Chinese takeaways in Ireland.

I suppose everyone looks back fondly on their teenage years, and like the young people say these days 'we thought we were all that' but the proof is in the potato as my best mates from back then are still my best mates. I lost my heart to a few lovely Irish girls and a little more to a French girl. I'm still close to my family and I still have a soft spot for seventies rock. But soon it was time to grow up…I was heading for my grown up life in the factory, and I couldn't wait!

Even with a carton of crisps under me I could barely see out the window.
Me here with the Head Honchos, Paddy Lillis, Ben Kealy and Kevin Masterson

Beatrice
Tayto
VIVA LAS TAYTO!
Nevada has the famous Las Vegas sign, Coolock has the famous Tayto one!
did Las Vegas get the idea for their famous sign from us?!
Who needs Las Vegas, when you have Coolock!

FACTORY YEARS

I COULDN'T WAIT TO GET STARTED IN THE FACTORY AND I WASN'T TOO PROUD TO START AT THE BOTTOM.

I sorted spuds in the stores, checked the seasoning in the flavour room, monitored the quality control on the assembly line, all the way through to checking the finished bags. And sampling one or two! In all my life I've never tired of the taste of Tayto!

By the early 1980's Da had taken a step back and now that I knew the run of the place, I was taking over! I finally had the chance to put my stamp on the factory, and the first thing I was going to do was branch out. Not all my new ideas worked. First up, I had a brainwave to make a "Classic Irish Wedding" set of crisps. Prawn Cocktail, following by Chicken and Ham, and then a revolutionary sweet crisp - Black Forest Gateaux. I had high hopes for my wedding crisps - they were the future! But only the prawn cocktail caught on. The others didn't do well at all - outside of Leitrim. I had to start thinking outside the bag.

The 1980's was a bad time in Ireland. A bit like these days to be honest only the panini hadn't even been invented to make things a little easier. Loads of people around Coolock went off to England or America and times were tough. But they say great ideas are born out of recession and I was determined to prove it. I walked around the city taking inspiration from the people. In fact it was the young fellas on their BMXs

in the Northside Shopping Centre carpark that gave me the idea for Wheelies. I invented Mighty Munch as a treat for the local kids at Halloween and they caught on. Chipsticks were created one night when our local chipper was closed for the pest controllers. I thought, what if you could get salt and vinegar chip style crisps? Presto - Chipsticks! So you see? Recessions aren't all bad! Get out there and start thinking people! Of course, for every good idea, there are a few bad ones…..but all you have to do is look back at my wedding menu crisps for that.

Despite the fact that things were tough, everyone supported each other back then. It was all about Guaranteed Irish and shopping local. We were involved in all sorts of sponsorship - we even tried to get a Tayto team to the Tour de France. We could only afford one bike the first year, so it was more of a relay. But by year two, we had two bikes. But with two fellas on each bike, we were never going to give Stephen Roche a run for his money - or should that be a ride!

We'd have family days out where there'd be all sorts of potato related fun. You've heard of egg n' spoon? We had crisp n' cushion! And then there was the sack race. But when the sack is full of potatoes, it's harder than you'd think…

It was great being the boss and during the eighties I relished being able to get inventive as new technologies and machinery were allowing us to create all kinds of new products. We were no longer stuck to just slicing spuds; there were extruders, moulding machinery and all kinds of hoppers, choppers and loppers and people seemed at long last to be more open to trying new flavours and new types of snacks. Sure before the mid-eighties came along, the only Irish people that travelled abroad bought a one way ticket. But now the Irish were starting to become a lot more sophisticated, and they wanted as many options in snacks as they were starting to see in life - like Jonnie Onion Rings - sure everyone knows you can't get more sophisticated than the French. But the point was, I had arrived. I was at the helm of the Good Ship Tayto, and we were on course for success!

Tayto Tour De France Team 1982 - with the recession we could only afford one bike.

Tayto Tour de France team 1984 - times were looking up as we now had two bikes.

The ROSE *of* TRALEE

FOR SOMEONE WHO LOOKS THIS GOOD IN A JACKET, I WAS THE PERFECT CANDIDATE TO BE AN ESCORT AT THE ULTIMATE 'LOVELY GIRL' COMPETITION 'THE ROSE OF TRALEE'.

My mate Coyler's brother had been an escort a couple of years back and said that he got lucky with the Californian Rose, as the American girls were 'far looser' than Irish girls. Remember this was the Seventies in Ireland, which is the equivalent of the Forties in America when it came to 'gettin off'. So myself, Coyler, Quinner, Doyler and Micko borrowed suits that fit from anyone we knew working in an office and we lined up with all the other hopefuls for the Escort interviews. There was hundreds of twenty something lads all equally uncomfortable in tins of fruit. Some ould boot came out with a clipboard and called us in one by one. Only the thought of a hand up the blouse of a beautiful foreign cailín kept us going. Since 1959, the selection committee, which was a nun, the fella that sings the song and a stern woman had been spotting chancers from a mile away, by smelling breath for booze, smelling pits for hygiene and asking questions about morals that would catch most spoofers out! But Coyler's brother had been training us for weeks, so we knew what to expect at the interrogation. Quinner was a non-runner from the get go as when asked, "What qualities does he admire most in a Rose?" he answered " As long as she's not a stuck up cow, I don't care!" Being subtle was never one of his greatest qualities. I was quite nervous when my turn came and although I had a load of stock answers prepared, in the end I just spoke my mind as the more I thought about it, being an escort at the famous Rose of Tralee would actually be a great honour. I think it paid off as the committee seemed impressed with the way I carried myself and my honest approach, well, except for the total lie that my favourite

him was 'The Sound of Music' because of the songs and how Julie Andrews is such an inspirational woman when it was actually 'Rocky' 'cause there was some great fighting in it! Only me and Coyler actually made it to Tralee that August, and we were determined to have a good time as we were glad to see the back of three weeks of 'waltz' training with Coyler's Ma (who always held me a little too tight for comfort). I was paired up with a lovely girl from Texas called Nora, she was the perfect Rose contestant, a bit of a looker and unlike what Coyler's brother had implied was a real lady. Coyler himself got landed with the Waterford Rose, who wasn't having any of it and within a day he had already earned a yellow card for dropping the hand during the opening ceremony dance. We had to go everywhere with the girls; horse riding, rowing on the lakes and photo calls with the papers.

Most of the other escorts were good craic, except for a couple of gobdaws from the Southside who did it every year! So what! Get a girlfriend! I got on with Nora and her 'folks' as she called them, who were over cheering on their girl and were pretty impressed that I was a Tayto, as her Da was an emigrant and one of the things he missed was our famous family crisps. One thing I hadn't expected was how competitive it all got on the nights of the show. All the escorts nerves were shot as in turn their Rose took to the stage and got a grilling from Gay Byrne. Some of them did great with the questioning, but then would blow it with their 'turns', with some ferocious warbling and falling on their arses during a jig. After spending a few days with Nora, I knew she had that X factor quality and I held my breath all through her bit. And when she sang 'The Yellow Rose of Texas' with an Irish lilt, I knew I was falling for her. Her beautiful eyes, her warm sense of humour and her great arse had won me over. But I had been warned as more often than not this happens to all the escorts. Well, except Coyler who was sent home early as he was caught trying on his Rose's dress; he's such a pervy weirdo! Anyway, back to Nora and me. We all thought she'd done a winning performance, but it wasn't to be, as the London Rose stole the heart of the judges that year. Nora had stolen my heart, but I knew she had a fella back in Dallas and besides those long distance relationships never work out. But I'll never forget that summer when I pretended to be a real gentleman. Speaking of gentlemen, the one thing my Ma asked me was to get Gaybo's autograph, I was pretty embarrassed asking the legendary Gay Byrne to sign something and get my photo taken with him, but it was no bother to him and being a true Dub, he knew all about my family business and promised that I could bring my Ma and Da into the Late Late Show audience anytime at all. Sound man that Gaybo, real Salt 'n' Vinegar of the earth type! To this day I still send over a box of my best to Nora at Christmas. She's loads of kids now and has been married three times! And despite my romantic notions that summer in Tralee, back in the Seventies, I have no intention of being number four. The real irony is that Coyler met his Rose again two years later at a Furey Brothers gig in Tramore…. and got off

FACTORY FILLIES

OF COURSE THE FACTORY WAS FIRST AND FOREMOST ABOUT THE CRISPS - BUT THE TAYTO FACTORY GIRLS WERE LEGENDARY.

Tayto Top Totty Awards 1972

Looking back now, I reckon we should have done a Tayto factory girls calendar before Michael O'Leary started doing it. Fierce sexy bunch they were and think of the arty shots you could get in a crisp factory! Women in a tabard and hair net and not much else, sexy spud handling, or American Beauty style in a bath of taters....you get the idea! But I don't think Ireland would have been ready for something like that back in the '70s.

But there was one girl who stood out from all the others in my eyes. Beatrice Murphy... Ah, beautiful Bea! She worked in Quality Control and she had the highest standards of anyone in that department. She wore a white coat, tight hair-net and plastic shoe covers and used to tap her nails off her clipboard in a way that'd drive a man wild.

Beatrice, my first girlfriend forever immortalised in truck form. A blonde bombshell with a solid chassis.

The tradition of naming trucks after girls continued with Brenda the foxy redhead.

Then there was Cathy from Kimmage...she was a big girl.

Then there's that horrible moment when your girlfriend bumps into your Ex!!

Of course it's all done by computers now. Here's Concepta and Mary, our top crisp counters in 1969.

And after work, when she took off her hairnet and shook her hair out it was like one of those shampoo ads you'd see nowadays. There was always a lovely smell of onions off her. All the fellas fancied Beatrice so I never thought I had a chance. Until one Friday evening at one of our social nights, I was telling her about a film that was coming to the local cinema I wanted to see. She said she wanted to see it too so I told her what day it was starting. When she went off to powder her nose one of the lads said "Ah Tayto, she wanted you to ask her to the cinema!". I hadn't copped on at all!

So when she came back, with a bit of dutch courage on me, I asked her would she come and see Grease with me the following Saturday. My potato heart skipped a beat when she said yes! I was walking on air the whole rest of the week. Me and Bea - I couldn't believe it.

We met outside the Savoy and I gave her a kiss on the cheek. I bought our tickets and some popcorn and when we left the cinema that night, we were a real life Danny and Sandy. The lads couldn't believe I'd bagged a girl like Beatrice. And neither could I. Days spent winking across the factory at her. I remember those long, hot summer nights in 1979, just me, Beatrice and a six pack down by the river. I thought I'd be with Bea forever but it wasn't to be. Three short months after our first date, she got a job in a chocolate factory. I was devastated but told her it didn't have to change anything. But within a few weeks she had dumped me for the head of Quality Control over there.

Ah, do you ever really get over your first love? I named the first Tayto truck of our fleet after Beatrice, a tradition I continued for a few girlfriends after her. I told her about it when I bumped into her a few years back and she was chuffed. She ended up marrying the chocolate bloke and they had a few kids. It was great to see her…and she still smelled of onions.

MY GREATEST HITS

I'VE SAID IT BEFORE AND I'LL SAY IT AGAIN, THE ONLY BOYBAND I LIKE COME FROM ARTANE.

And since this book is all about me 'fork and knife' I thought you might be interested in what flavour of music Ireland's number one Spud digs. As a young spud I was a bit of a rocker around town, whilst Ma and Pa where dancing to the showband sounds of Dickie Rock and Brendan Boyer, I was spinning me 45's at full volume and jumping around the bedroom to Cream, Led Zeppelin and Jimi Hendrix. If I had any hair, I would have grown it long to be just like my rock idols. " If you think it's too loud, you're too old" I used to tell Pa. Mind you some of the "Oompf, Oompf' stuff they do be playing nowadays is fierce noisy altogether…oh do you hear me, I've become my Pa! Mind you, it'll never again be like Dublin in the early Seventies when we were all jammed tighter than a multi pack of Tayto, into the Baggot Inn, or the TV Club on Harcourt Street banging our heads to Lizzy, The Horslips and Taste. Ah, those were the days when the price of a gig was half the price of a pint. Two of my all time musical heroes from that time were proud Irishmen through and through; one was Rory Gallagher, the guitarist from Taste (mind you, I never did find out what his favourite flavour was!) and our own man in black, Phil Lynott.

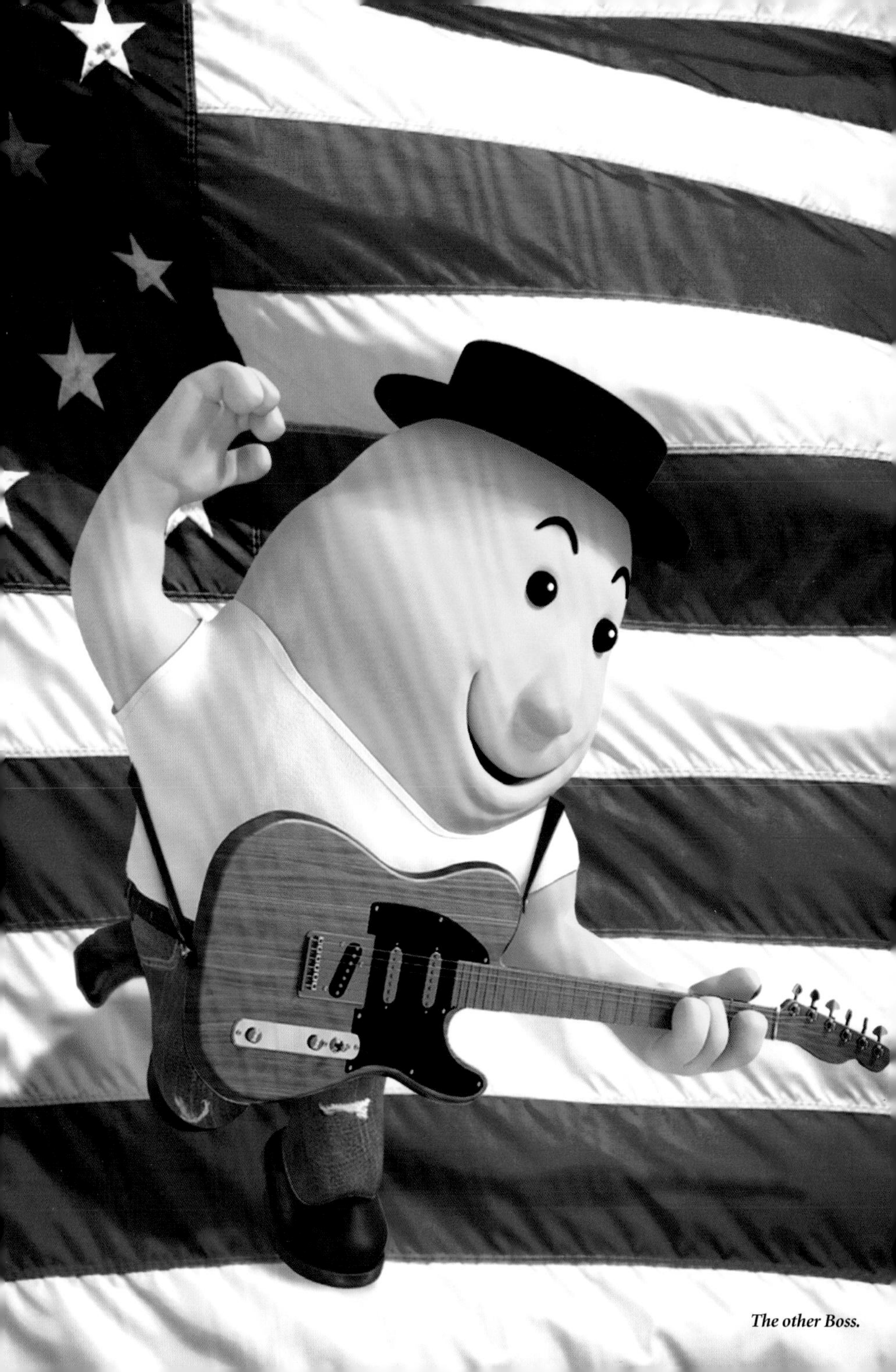

The other Boss.

If Rory hadn't become one of the fastest guitar slingers on the scene, I think he could have been a great peeler in the factory. I met Phillo himself a couple of times over the years and I'd always stick a few boxes of Cheese and Onion in the back of the tour bus, so they could have a taste of home when they were off touring the world. And I could be wrong but I think this line from The Boys Are Back in Town is about a bird he used see who was mad into the salt & vinegar, and she used to shake the bag before she'd burst it open;

"You know that chick that used to dance a lot. Every night she'd be on the floor shaking what she's got."

Mind you, I could be reading more into that than there is.

The Seventies wasn't my favourite time for music, I never got into the angry punk thing. The thought of sticking a skewer through me skin just to look 'different' didn't appeal. So I'm going to come clean now and admit that I was a disco spud! I went to all the clubs like Zhivago and threw me red jacket over me shoulder, opened my shirt down low, revealing my medallion and boogie'd with the best of them. Here's me doing my best Travolta circa 77!

After disco died I was very wary of following the trends of the time and besides I was getting a bit older and wiser. Instead of following the Top of the Pops, I started getting back into real homegrown music. Moving Hearts featuring one Christy Moore and Mr Donal Lunny caught this spuds attention and songs like Bagatelle's 'Summer in Dublin' became the soundtrack to my life. After a hard days work in the factory I'd like nothing more than going for a pint with good friends and seeing Christy spin a story with his music.

As the business grew and Tayto became Top of the Crisps, I'd less time for music, but I watched with pride (in the name of love!) as the bould U2, Sinead O'Connor and The Cranberries took over the world.

Then it all seemed to go 'spuds up' with the boyband explosion. It's probably my age, but they seem more concerned about their hair than the music. Now don't get me wrong, they're nice fellas and they're making a bleedin' fortune, but should they really be at the top of the charts where The Beatles, T-Rex and Bowie used to be?

As for the new wave of reality show chart toppers, I'll get me red coat!

So there yis have it, like any kid, I was mad into music, and nowadays I tend to listen to the old stuff all over again. I still have that old record player from my bedroom, that caused the ceiling to come down into the kitchen one Saturday night, but that's another story! And the odd time I'll throw on a bit of Zeppelin or Lizzy and be transported right back, and the odd time, I'm not ashamed to say, I'll step into those platforms, swing that jacket over my shoulder and 'Tony Manaro' me way around the gaff. The neighbour's kid, caught me shaking my stuff one day to 'More than a Woman' and called me 'Mr.Gayto', but I couldn't care less!

As Prince once said to me backstage at the RDS when I personally delivered a few bags of his favourite Smokey Bacon, "Mr.Tayto, you're one salty MF!".

The cheesiest thing about this photo? It's not the crisps!

Part Two

MATURE CHEESE

THE 1980'S GETS VERY BAD PRESS THESE DAYS. BUT IT WASN'T ALL DOOM AND GLOOM - HOW COULD ANY DECADE BE ALL BAD WHEN WE HAD ROLLER DISCOS, LEG WARMERS, BAD PERMS AND STONEWASHED DENIM!

Here's me trying to blag a trip on Celtic Mist, but Charlie was having none of it!

This was the Ireland of Charlie Haughey, moving statues and H Williams supermarkets. We were being put on the map with the likes of U2 taking the world by storm, and put on the cheesy map by Johnny Logan winning the Eurovision about a million times! And the Dart was introduced. It is believed that some of the original rubbish dumped back in 1984 can still be found on Dart trains today. Who needs museums! The Irish people got their first National Lottery, and we put our cards on the table when we offered several well-known people the freedom of Dublin City to mark the millennium celebrations in 1988, (including Nelson Mandela, which to be honest, was a bit ironic as he was still in prison).

The '80s were a great time for me. I bought my first car - a Toyota Corolla, and my first house - a semi-d out near the factory in Coolock. I can't say I didn't miss the buzz of life in Moore Street, but sure half the lads were still there so I was back every other weekend. I know every decade says this, but they were simpler times. If you had a television, it didn't have a remote control, (yes, you had to walk to the television set, imagine that!), people had a Rubik's Cube instead of a Nintendo DS and a Lo-Lo ball was an acceptable form of transport. No one had an iPod; if you wanted portable music you dragged around a twin deck ghetto blaster, which took about twenty D batteries, and weighed about three stone. Then as the 1980's rolled in, the privileged few had cassette Walkmans - naturally Quinner was the first to get one as he drove a lot for work, and collected Maxol tokens from the local garage for it. It was that or a 'Free a Nipper'. So Quinner would sit down the back of the bus when we headed out for a night, with his Walkman on full blast, until he got the headphone wires caught one day, and it smashed to smithereens as it hit the floor. He was gutted. They weren't built to last those Walkmans. Home computers were the stuff of the future, so we went down the arcade to play Donkey Kong, Pac Man and Super Mario Bros - hey, you're never too old for the arcades! Culture Club, Dexy's Midnight Runners and Madonna were on the radio, Sam Fox was on our walls, and we all thought Elton John and George Michael were straight!

We may have been all grown up, buying cars and gaffs, but we were still young enough to make holy shows of ourselves! The lads and I strutted around town on a Saturday night trying to impress the ladies; me and Quinner in our Don Johnson jackets and baggy trousers, Coyler with his skinny black and white piano tie and a mullet, Micko in his 'Frankie Says Relax' t-shirt (he had three in different colours) and Doyler in whatever he'd seen in the cinema or on telly that week. Quinner went a bit yuppie on us for a while, and he was the first person in the country to have a mobile phone. Well, I say 'mobile', but it was about as mobile as a phone box! But he loved pretending to make calls on it down the pub; of course he wouldn't actually make many real calls as each call cost him about the price of my car. But even though we hate to admit it - it did impress the girls! Mind you, he also stuck a strip of red lighting to the front of his black Opel Kadett pretending he was Knightrider....that didn't impress them as much!

Doyler was forever trying out new things on a whim. We got great mileage out of him! He grew a moustache (not very successfully) after Magnum PI, took up martial arts after seeing The Karate Kid (lasted a week until he broke a rib), and I won't even go into what we had to put up with after he saw Raiders of the Lost Ark. Needless to say, we all refused to refer to him as Indiana Doyle.

There was one weekend when I decided to host a drinks party at my house - sure the whole point of buying your own place is so you can have a party whenever you like isn't it? All the lads were coming, and we'd asked a load of girls from the local and the factory; we made sure the odds were stacked in our favour! The night was set for Saturday, the ghetto blaster was primed with a copy of Now That's What I Call Music 4 and I had the nibbles sorted - cheese and pineapple cubes on sticks, napkin-lined baskets of Tayto, and cocktail sausages. It was all set to be a night to remember. Micko was in charge of cocktails, and that's where it all went wrong. He had found a recipe for the latest trendy drink - Harvey Wallbangers. It was made of vodka, orange juice and some fancy liquor that sounded like galley-something. Of course, we couldn't find it anywhere, so Micko reckoned Baileys would do, as that was fierce sophisticated. No one can quite remember how the night ended, but Quinner woke up in the front yard with a cheese and pineapple stick in his forehead, Coyler was found in the kitchen with the Now cassette tape pulled apart and wound around his head and none of the girls from the factory would speak to us for months. We didn't try making cocktails after that. I'm just glad mobile phones weren't around back then or someone would have videoed the whole thing!

By the end of the 1980's, the country was pulling itself out of the recession and things were looking up. In 1990, we got our first lady-president Mary Robinson and our first pound coin (whichever you were more excited about depended on your age!). As the nineties moved on, the first signs of the Celtic Tiger (or Celtic Tater as I like to call it!) were starting to show. The boom was fast approaching, people were starting to hear about a little thing called the Internet, we got ourselves another cute hoo-er of a Taoiseach in the shape of

Bertie Ahern, unemployment virtually disappeared and we all had access to great new television channels (and TG4). Cheesy music gave way to hip hop which gave way to grunge; and on the other side of the coin, boy and girl bands took over the world. Big budget films like Jurassic Park and Titanic were at the box office and the Irish abroad started to come home again.

And so it was time to head into the new millennium....

"There's one for everyone in the audience"
Except he meant one crisp - Pat kept the rest for himself!

ANDREWS Chris
O'CALLAGHAN Jim
VOTE 1, 2 in order of your choice
FIANNA FÁIL
www.mrtayto.ie
MISTER
TAYTO
VOTE No. 1
1
TAYTO YOUR ONLY MAN

ELECTION CAMPAIGN 2007

HUMBLE SPUD

THERE'S A TIME IN EVERY MAN'S LIFE WHEN HE REFLECTS ON HIS ACHIEVEMENTS SO FAR AND HOW WHAT HE'S LEARNT COULD FLAVOUR FUTURE GENERATIONS.

2007 was the year, with Bertie knee deep in Tribunals that I felt a different potato head altogether was what the country needed! It felt like change was in the air. The business side of things was running smoothly so I could put all my efforts into a tasty campaign.

First things first I had to come clean and make sure there were no tasty tabloid secrets that might come out and bite me on the arse. But I've always prided myself on being a clean spud, a straight cut potato, despite anything you may have read or heard about me!

And so with my agenda in place, the campaign started in earnest. I hired a campaign manager and running mate, one of my old pals and one of Ireland's funniest men, Frank Kelly. Sure everyone loves Father Jack, and you couldn't ask for a better Tánaiste could you?

We put posters up on every lamppost in the land, with my face battling against Enda Kenny, Pat Rabitte and Trevor Sargent. If it was a beauty contest I'd have won hands down! But unfortunately it wasn't, it was a ferocious contest with lots of name calling, back stabbing, and debating. But I was determined not to lower myself to that level. I wasn't too proud to wish the other contestants, I mean candidates, well. I met Labour Party leader, Eamon Gilmore outside Government Buildings on Merrion Square and shook his hand. I'm not sure he knew what to make of me, but I could tell by the look in his eyes, he knew he had stiff competition. After that I even took the time to drive around to the offices of Labour, Fine Gael and Fianna Fáil in Dublin to deliver them boxes of crisps and a bit of good-natured banter!

But despite my best efforts to play fair, I got myself into some pretty hot water over the course of the campaign. In Killarney, Frank and myself were ambushed by Jackie and Michael Healy Rae. I must have had them rattled to resort to such low tactics. It was far from plain sailing, the people loved me, but the authorities didn't!

Ambushed by Jackie and Michael Healy Rae!

PACK-IT-IN:

"Mister Tayto and his director of elections, Frank Kelly, got more than they bargained for on the campaign trail in Killarney. They were ambushed by hostile natives in the guise of a poll rival, TD Jackie Healy Rae and his son Michael, director of elections of the Healy Rae Campaign."

EVENING HERALD TUESDAY 15TH MAY 2007

MR. TAYTO ON
CLIMATE CHANGE
"I DON'T SEE ANYTHING WRONG WITH A WEEK OR TWO IN THE CANARIES."

MR. TAYTO ON
HIS CABINET
"IT'S SOLID MAHOGANY WITH A LOVELY SILVER INLAY."

MR. TAYTO ON
TRANSPORT
"I PROMISE A METRO IN DUBLIN BY 3012."

MR. TAYTO ON
THE HOLE IN THE OZONE LAYER
"IT IS OF THE UTMOST IMPORTANCE THAT WE LOOK INTO IT."

MR. TAYTO ON
GAY MARRIAGE
"HE'S REMARRYING? DOES KATHLEEN KNOW?"

MR. TAYTO ON
PEACE AND RECONCILIATION
"IT'S TIME THAT THE NORTH AND SOUTHSIDE LEARNED TO LIVE TOGETHER."

For more information on the Mr. Tayto election campaign and to download his song please visit www.mrtayto.ie
For latest Election Odds visit www.irishelectionbetting.com

VOTE TAYTO IRELAND'S NO. 1

Please dispose of this leaflet responsibly

My election flyer.

SUMMONS

AN CHUIRT DUICHE:
District Court Area of Dungarvan:
COURTS (NO.3) ACT, 1986, SECTION 1

THE DISTRICT COURT
District No. 21

Reference:092004
Prosecutor: Dungarvan Town Council

Accused: **MISTER TAYTO** INTELLECTUAL PROPERTIES LIMITED,

Of: KILBREW
ASHBOURNE
CO. MEATH

WHEREAS on the 16th day of April 2007 an application was made to this office by John Dwane on behalf of the above named Prosecutor for the issue of a summons to you, the above named Accused, of the above address, alleging the following offence:-

THAT you were on the 11th day of December 2006 at in the Court area and District aforesaid the registered owner of Vehicle No. 03-KK-1989 which was parked at

GLANBIA CAR PARK, DUNGARVAN, CO. WATERFORD
without a valid Road Fund Licence displayed and you did thereby commit an offence under Section 73(1) of the Finance Act 1976.

THIS IS TO NOTIFY YOU that you will be accused of the said offence at a sitting of the District Court to be held at The Courthouse, Dungarvan, Co. Waterford on the 23rd day of May 2007 at 10:30am AND TO REQUIRE YOU to appear at the said sitting to answer the said accusation.

National Irish Bank
www.nationalirishbank.ie
For 24 hour banking call 1850 200400

P.O. BOX. 109A
27 COLLEGE GREEN
DUBLIN 2

Date 30th April 07

Pay Dungarvan Town Council
One hundred + twenty eight Euro Only

€ 128-00

Ireland

I was given litter fines from all over the country when my posters were reported as illegal - I paid them and wore them as a badge of honour. The opposition were really out to get me!

Notice in relation to an alleged offence under the Litter Pollution Act, 1997
Fógra I ndáil le cion líomhnaithe faoin Acht um Thruailliú ó Bhruscar, 1997

29 MAY 2007

To/Chuig Name/Ainm Mister Tayto

Address/Seoladh Kilbrew, Ashbourne, Co. Meath

Serial No./Sraithuimhir 5541

It is alleged that you have committed an offence under Section 19 of the Litter Pollution Act, 1997
See overleaf for details of alleged offence

Líomhnáitear go ndearna tú cion faoi .... den Acht um Thruailliú ó Bhruscar, 1997
Féach thall le haghaidh shonraí an chiona líomnaitear

On the/Ar an 15 Day of/Lá de 05 Year/Blian 07 Tuesday 10.05

at/i junction of Castle Street and Verdant Place, King's Island (Illegal Erection of Advertising Posters) additional fines may follow.

and that a mechanically propelled vehicle with the identification mark was used in the commission of the offence:

agus gur úsáideadh feithicil innealghluaiste leis an Marc aitheantais ag déanamh an chiona:

A prosecution in respect of the alleged offence will not be instituted during the period of 21 days beginning on the date of this notice and, if during that period you pay to

Ní thionscnófar ionchúiseamh maidir leis an gcion líomhnaithe I rith na tréimhse 21 lá dar tosach dáta an fhógra seo agus, le linn na tréimhse sin, má íocann tú suim €

Name of Local Authority/Ainm an Údaráis Áitiúil/Address/Seoladh LIMERICK CITY COUNCIL

Mr Tayto could be fined a packet

City Council confirmed that Tayto posters are being taken down. Officials in Dun Laoghaire/Rathdown, Fingal, South Dublin and all the county councils around the country are likely to follow suit.

But, even if he is forced to take his message off the country's lampposts, Mr Tayto intends to continue his billboard campaign.

And following the lead from many of the country's other politicians, he has taken to the internet to sell his message.

Already, he has set up a website advertising his policies and giving details of his daily campaign trail. Yesterday was spent meeting voters in Wicklow and Wexford.

He has also launched an in-depth manifesto dealing with topics such as climate change, gay marriage, space exploration, illiteracy and whaling.

MISTER TAYTO VOTE No. 1

SPOT THE SPOOFER?: Fine Gael leader Enda Kenny looks bemused by Tayto poster

Drink! Girls! Crisps! Vote! Serious fun on election trail

FINE GAEL'S Enda Kenny and Mr. Tayto's election agent, Frank Kelly share a joke outside Kenny's pub in Lucan last week. The deep-fried potato candidate was also on hand to debate critical issues such as class sizes ("never less than 12 foo by 9 foot") and peace and reconciliation ("the north and southsid need to learn to live together.")

Lucan Gazette Wednesday 23rd May 2007

Enda Kenny may have been laughing loud, but he knew he was in for some stiff competition!

But even during the low times, it was the Irish people that kept me going. Getting out and about and meeting the public was the best part of the whole campaign. I kissed that many babies my face smelled of Farley's Rusks. I shook hands with thousands of people and had a few phone numbers slipped into my jacket pocket (you know who you are, ladies!). I travelled through Louth and Meath, down through Bray, Wicklow and Wexford, drove my bus on down to Waterford and Kilkenny, and headed to Cork. I knocked on doors and waved at planes. I was interviewed on every local radio station that would let me in. Everywhere I went people came out to see me. I doubt even Barack Obama would get that much attention driving around Ireland on a double decker bus! I went to Limerick on the way back up, and bumped into Pat Rabitte. I'm not going to lie; he was clearly threatened by my popularity. But who could blame him? He wasn't the only one - on a tour of the midlands a little later in the campaign, the Tayto election bus wouldn't fit under a bridge in Longford, and to this day, I'm not convinced the opposition didn't have it lowered! And in Galway, I had a football kicked at my head in Eyre Square, knocking my hat clean off and I can't be sure as I was a little dazed, but I still think I saw Michael Kitt running in the opposite direction. Now that's playing dirty!

When Paddy Power had to take out extra insurance to cover all the bets they'd taken in on me becoming the next Taoiseach, I knew I was giving the parties a run for their money!! I hadn't even been given the training the other politicians had, ya know, the knack for answering questions without actually giving an answer! As the contest was coming to an end I came to the conclusion that politics and potatoes didn't really mix. Having said that, I certainly made my potato stamp on the country. I got loads of votes - more than folk realise - and in Carlow-Kilkenny, where I secured over 700 votes, some enthusiastic supporters stapled their empty Tayto packets to their ballots, when they voted "Tayto No. 1"!!

5541

…d in respect of the illegal erection of an advertising sign on a Limerick City …il Decorative Post at the junction of Castle Street and Verdant Place, Island. Photograph taken at 10.06 on Tuesday 15th May, 2007.

Mr Tayto must remove Wexford election posters

■ Mr.

MR. TAYTO could be in trouble if all his election posters were not taken down during his campaign visit to the town last.

Only registered candidates in the General Election are given an exemption from the fly-posting laws to erect posters during the run-up to May 24.

Tayto have jumped on the political bandwagon with a clever advertising campaign comprising whistle-stop tours around the country, backed up with posters and billboards.

The posters depict Mr. Tayto as 'your only man' and urge voters to give him their Number 1. The billboards are a bit more puzzling – one refers to the candidate and his mahogany cabinet and another says – 'Mr. Tayto on gay marriage. (He is remarrying, does Kathleen know?)'.

No-one except the agents acting on behalf of a nominated candidate are entitled to put up posters.

Mr. Tayto's campaign team said they only put the posters up in a town on the day he arrives and take them down that evening.

But, according to Environment Officer, Tony Nolan, any Mr. Tayto posters left on poles would be in breach of the Litter Pollution Act and action would have to be taken.

WEXFORD PEOPLE - 16TH MAY 2007

By **Kevin Doyle**

MISTER Tayto is in hot water even before his potential political career begins.

The quirky candidate, who has been erecting posters all around the country as part of a novel advertising campaign, could be forced to take them down within hours or face fines running into thousands of euro.

The posters, which have already been spotted around Dublin, Tipperary and particularly in Ashbourne where Mr Tayto owns a buffalo ranch, have been rolled out as a parody of the real election candidates.

However, under council guidelines only official TD wannabes are allowed erect posters and, in Dublin at least, the city council is "actively" taking away any illegal signs.

The large posters which carry full length pictures of Mr Tayto and the catchphrase "Your only man" fall outside a loophole in the Litter Pollution Act that allows official candidates erect their posters.

A spokesperson for Dublin

EVENING HERALD - 11TH MAY 2007

Result's in the bag

"PAT Rabbitte had a chip on his shoulder yesterday - thanks to Mr. Tayto. The Labour Leader got off to a crisp start with agent Frank Kelly in Limerick despite this potato-headed stunt. However, Mr. Rabbitte told onlookers that he was ready for the crunch election in two weeks' time."

IRISH DAILY MAIL - WEDNESDAY 16TH MAY 2007

When I say my supporters were the driving force behind my campaign - I meant it literally!

One great thing that came out of my Royston-esque foray into politics was that I realised that there truly was something missing from my life. But it wasn't a calling into politics, it was a different calling entirely; it was the call of Cupid. And so with the election trail behind me, I was now on the trail for love. For so many years I'd been a single care free spud, living the life of a Dublin bachelor, but even a spudmuffin like me dreams of settling down, finding a wife and ya never know, maybe a couple of chipsticks running around.

The Election Ballad of Mr Tayto

Well, as everybody knows,
From Galway Bay to oul Montrose,
The country doesn't run on good intentions.
And the man that does the job
Will be the one that shuts his gob
And munches through the things that need attention.

But whatever the bosses say
At the end of a working day
You need a way to rest your weary knees.
Now the man that's on the case
Is red of coat and yellow of face
And he has the taste of unn-y-in and cheese.

Chorus

Mr. Tayyyyyyyyto! Mr. Tayyyyyyto!
The snack that has the knack for havin' the crack.
Vote for Tayyyyyyyto! Vote for Tayyyyyyto!
He'll always be the leader of the pack.

Now the lads in Leinster House
Have 50 ways of wrigglin out,
So when things go wrong, there's never a man at fault.
But from Cobh to Clontib-ret
The people never should forget
That we're a nation reared on vinegar and salts.

So get up, get on yer feet,
Support the candidate with teeth
And policies that aren't afraid to bite.
Cos he's a man that knows the score,
He'll tip his hat & close the door
On yer gombeen men, yer boyos and yer gobshites.

Chorus

Oh whenever he's pressin' flesh
He wears a smile that's always fresh.
His spirit never, ever seems to flag.
And all them skeptics have to do,
If they don't believe it's true,
Is check the date that's underneath his bag.

Chorus

SPUD MUFFIN

I'D BEEN INVOLVED IN MANY CAMPAIGNS OVER THE YEARS, FROM ELECTION CAMPAIGNS TO DRESSING UP AS SANTA FOR THE TAYTO CHRISTMAS BOXES, BUT THERE HAS NEVER BEEN A CAMPAIGN CLOSER TO MY HEART, LITERALLY, THAN MY SEARCH FOR MRS TAYTO.

We could have been the new Irish super-couple… "Glayto" anyone?

The lovely Kathryn Thomas had just won an IFTA when this photo was taken - Sure I didn't stand a chance

I used my experience in the election to launch a nationwide campaign to find a woman who could share my love of cheese & onion, who could be the salt to my vinegar, the smokey to my bacon (actually that sounds a bit rude); in short, I was ready to settle down. I've often been told I was one hot potato, a spud stud, and many claim I'm Ireland's most edible bachelor, and of course I've been associated with many famous Irish ladies over the years; from Glenda to Twink.

Then there were a couple of serious close calls to matrimony, but I was too young and free to simmer down at the time. And besides I think that one of them was only interested in getting at my well-stuffed packet! But after a lonely Crispmas of 2007, worn out from my electioneering, I did some sou searching and decided that this potato around town was ready to settle down. I knew I wasn't going to find wife material in my usual bachelor haunts; the VIP clubs or fancy restaurants.

So where on earth would I start? Coyler, who had recently enough got hitched himself after many years of bachelorising, told me all about how he'd met his missus on-line. I said that I didn't realise that there was a place that you could queue for one, but that's not what he meant of course. He meant on the grea cyberweb-superhighway computer.

Now I know it's well into the "noughties", and I might know me way around a chipstick, but computer 'chips' are beyond me. The days of meeting a potential wife at a dancehall or in a pub are well and truly gone. Cyber dating speed dating and Internet chat rooms were all the rage. I was going to have to get computer literate if I wanted to keep up.

So I went for it, spud guns blazing! With a bit of help, I set up my own Facebook and Bebo pages. They each attract a different kind of person you see, and I always like to keep my options open. I've got an oniony quality to me in that way - lots of layers! Facebookers would be more the Bistro and Occasions eaters, and the Bebo brigade would be more likely to bring home a six pack of Cheese & Onion. We all know that life isn't a popularity contest but I think most people have more friends on Facebook than they've probably ever met in their life. I've got thousands up there. Not that you don't have to

Mr Tayto
http://mrtayto.typepad.com/mrtaytoblog/?gender=F&env=
Mr Tayto
LOOKING FOR LOVE
THE BLACKBOOK
CHEESY CHAT UP LINES
WELL TASTY STUFF
MEET MR TAYTO
LEGAL
ABOUT US
CHECK OUT OTHER CHAT UP LINES
Looking for Love
CATEGORIES
Cheesy stuff
Looking for Love
Lovely Girls
Out on the town
Romantic musings
The Love Bus
Wingmen of Ireland
'What is a nice girl like you doing in a dirty mind like mine?'
Andrew, all I can say is that if the don't fall for this they're obviously immune to high powered cheesiness.
Well done sir, and a box of Tayto is currently be prepared for your enjoyment.
7 MARCH 2008 | CHEESY STUFF | COMMENTS (0)

exercise a little caution when cyber-socialising. I was getting lovely messages from a Russian beauty called Svetlana who said she had heard all about Tayto and I ended up sending her several boxes.

I should have wondered when the address was an Irish PO box number, but she said she had them forwarded on as she didn't want me spending all that money on the postage to Russia. She sent me lovely messages about how finger licking good my crisps were and her profile photo was amazing - tall and blonde, she looked like one of those women that would live on an island in a James Bond film. She said she thought I looked a-peeling and we became firm cyber-buddies. I thought I might just have found my Mrs. Tayto, until I discovered five months later that sexy Svetlana was a fella from Borrisokane called Shay. He was in it for the crisps. Morto I was! Coyler started sending me texts signed 'Tatiana' and various Russian names, and all the lads took the almighty mickey out of me for a good few weeks!

Mind you, I've heard plenty of stories of people meeting on the Internet and living happily ever after, so I'll always keep an open mind! At the moment I'm even Tweeting with a fine cailín in Potato Town, Idaho (yes, there is such a place!) and we'll see where that one goes. But for now I'm quite happy staying 'just friends' with all my cyber acquaintances out there. And I have to admit the internet is a great way to meet new friends and stay in touch with old ones.

A while ago, I set up a Halloween dress-me-up page for my Bebo site and it all went a bit mad! So check out Bebo if you want to see me as a skating -1970's -vampire –Elvis-astronaut…or any other number of weird and wonderful combinations. The imagination of Tayto fans never fails to amaze me….and disturb me at the same time.

So then I went back to more basic means - the tried and trusted personal ads and very quickly I thought I might have met my Juliet. On paper she was perfect. But as is often the case with things that appear too good to be true they usually are! I arranged to meet her in an Italian restaurant in Temple Bar. I had a rose and everything. The next thing I know, the waiter came over with a note simply saying "I had a peek through the window and you're not

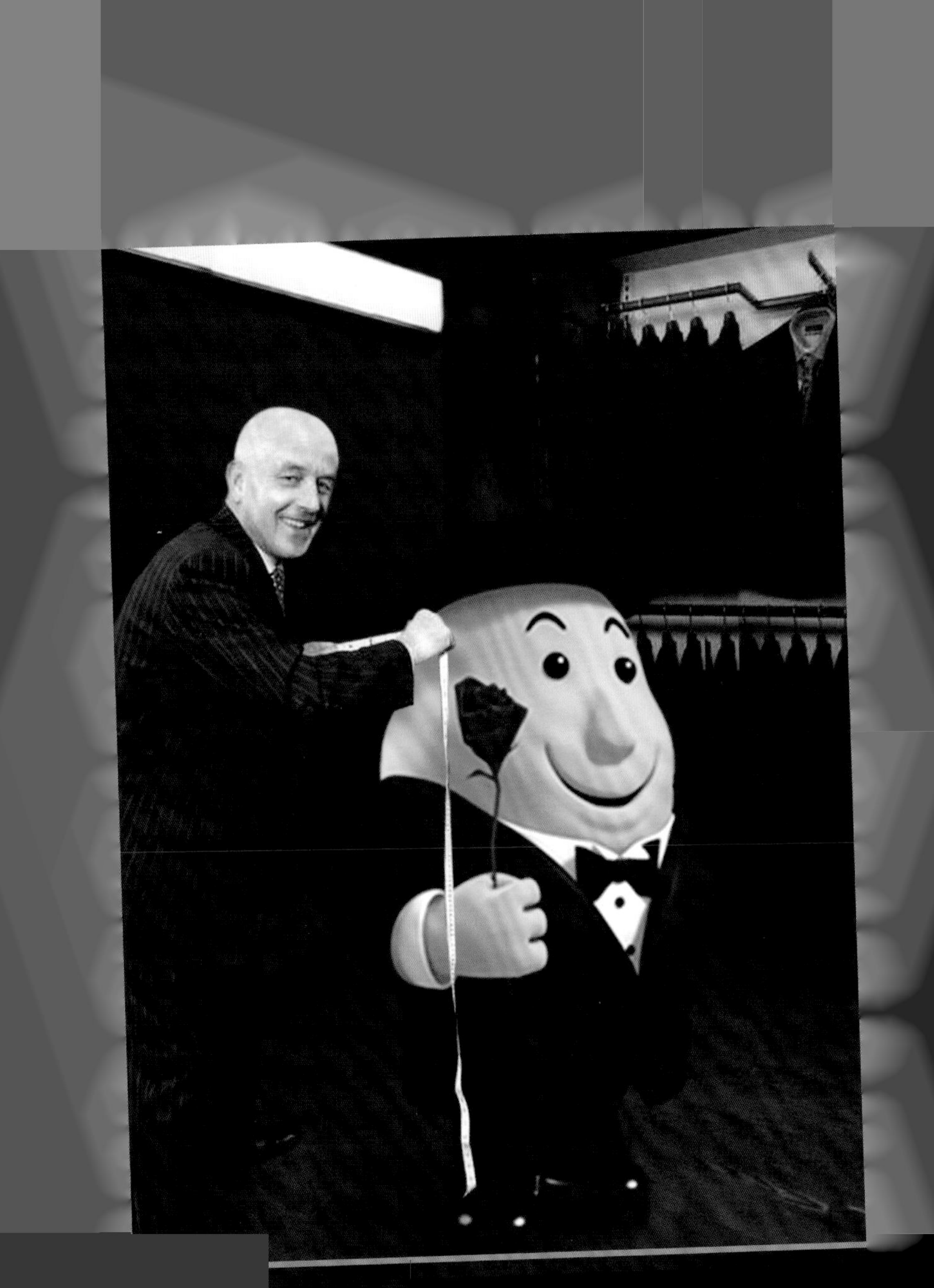

Legendary tailor

ONE HOT POTATO

HE'S BRINGING SEXY BACK

He's looking for a Mrs. Tayto.
To help go to www.mrtayto.ie

So I decided no more blind dates, no more internet set ups, I was going to take the same approach as I did in the elections - be up front and honest… and my now infamous poster ad campaign was born.

First things first and it was down to my old mate Louis Copeland for a brand new suit fitting. I needed to look sharp for the new posters. After he had me suited up I was ready for action. But what kind of woman is Ireland's most edible bachelor after? That got me thinking, what was my ideal lady? Well first off, she had to be a solid girl, beef to the heel type, you know? She needed to be down to earth, have a good sense of humour and a love of music. I'm not at all opposed to a woman who wears trousers; it shows a certain level of sophistication in my mind. And speaking of sophistication she had to be one that enjoyed the finer things in life, like a rainy afternoon knee-deep in mud at the ploughing championships eating crisp sandwiches! And I love a woman who looks good in a pair of wellies, but looks aren't everything, she'd want some brains too. I mean she'd definitely have to know the business end of a heifer.

And so the lovely cailíní of Ireland knew what tickled this spud's fancy and the challenge was on. But I was never one to be presumptuous and I knew I'd have to put some serious work into this search as well. And that's why I enlisted the talents of the men of Ireland, kindred spirits if you will, to help me navigate the long and winding road towards true love. And the wingmen of Ireland came through for this lonely potato by helping me get prepared for when I met Mrs Right with some of the greatest 'Chat Up Lines' known to man! And for their tireless work in the important art of breaking the ice, I will be forever indebted. You came through brothers, you came through!

And for any lonely bachelors reading this book, (and judging by the scale of Lisdoonvarna last summer, there are still quite a few), here's some of my favourite chat-her-uppers that the Cheese and Onion munching brothers sent in to me during my quest that you can use freely! No, I haven't tried them all, but the players of Ireland guaranteed they'd work.

The response to the search was unbelievable, so much so, that I simply couldn't open all the sack loads of mail I was receiving, so Micko's son came in and set up a website for all the ladies to mail me at. It was amazing that

My Best Chat up lines

"Excuse me. You owe me a drink. I looked at you & dropped mine".

"Will you come to the cinema? My mum says I can't go on my own."

"Well here I am. What were your other two wishes?"

'What is a nice girl like you doing in a dirty mind like mine?'

'Is there an airport around here or is that my heart taking off?'

'Your eyes are the same colour as my Porsche!'

'Me, Tarzan. You, lucky'

'You must be the reason for global warming, because you're so hot!'

"Can I have your picture? Cos I'll want to know I wasn't dreaming tomorrow...'

"If you were a burger at McDonalds, you'd be a McGorgeous"

"Do you believe in love at first sight, or should I walk by again?"

"I may be a frog but if you kiss me I'll turn into a prince"

"I just wanted to show this rose how incredibly beautiful you are!"

"There must be something wrong with my eyes, I can't take them off you."

"If I followed you home, would you keep me?"

"If I could rearrange the alphabet I'd put u and I together"

"Did it hurt when you fell from heaven?"

"I'm afraid you're under arrest.....for trespassing in my dreams"

Yes, they may be super cheesy, but once you've made a woman laugh, you're half way there compadres.

so many gorgeous Irish women were willing to take a chance on this simple Dublin spud. As the offers came in their thousands, I was really confident that there was a Mrs Tayto out there somewhere.

After a few months however, it was getting to crunch time for this full-flavoured gent, and I was no closer to a decision. Every day I received another love letter from a blonde, a red head or a brunette that would put my heart into a spin.

Just when you think you've found the woman of your dreams then you get a note from lovely Caroline from Limerick, you're sorely tempted to become a one woman man and tell the lads you're staying home with the missus for a Desperate Housewives DVD marathon. Caroline is not only lovelier than a lovely thing on St Lovely's day, she's also got yards of charm and poetic skill:

"Its crunch time for me and my love life, so I'd love to bag myself Mr Tayto aka The Stud Spud! Check out that crisp sharp suit, he's obviously a man of good taste! I could be your Mrs Tayto, your (Golden) Wonder Woman, I won't cost you a packet and I haven't got a chip on my shoulder! We could stay in and be couch potatoes or go out and bop to cheesy tunes. And when the chips are down, I'll still be at your side. And believe me, our love life would never go stale coz Mr T's one hot potato!!"

And just when my heart was all mashed up with Caroline's poetic turn and sultry looks, along comes another love note from Dublin beauty Ann Marie who describes herself as looking for;

'A good all rounder' and 'is going to show me a smashing time!'

So then Ann Marie's stolen my heart…until yet another Dub; Ciara bowls me over with her blonde locks and this heart melting one liner:

"I'm ur new yet to be released flavour
SWEET HONEY LIPS"

Better Stop There Before I Boil Over!

ARE YOU A LOVELY GIRL?

♥♥♥

Tall, yellow and loveable
spud muffin, would like to meet
beef to the heel cailíns
interested in long-term romance.
Must look good in overalls
and know the crucial difference
between a bull and a bullock.
To make the connection
log onto
www.mrtayto.ie

ARE YOU A LOVELY GIRL

♥♥♥

Giant spud, looking for the cheese
to his onion, would like to meet
well-heeled lovelies interested
in becoming a missus.
Turn-ons include wellies,
shawls and pipes. Knowing the
business end of a heifer
a plus. To make
the connection
log onto
www.mrtayto.ie

ARE YOU A LOVELY GIRL?

Potato shaped individual would like
to meet, thick ankled lovelies
with marriage in mind.
Must enjoy the finer things in life
like a spin in a Massey Ferguson,
crisp sandwiches, and a good old
knees up. If your turn-ons
include wellies, snacks and
a bloke in a hat, I'm your only man.
To make the connection
log onto
www.mrtayto.ie

So now you can see my dilemma. The idea of laying my heart out to woman seemed like a good idea, but instead of finding one Mrs Tayto, literally sack-fulls of eligible brides to be. And after getting the opport to do a photo shoot with a bevy of beauties, I finally realised what the ar to my love quest was.

Like my famous multi-packs, I decided there should be enough of me t around for everyone. So I wrote a letter to all the ladies who'd contrib to my now overflowing black book, and thanked them all for making me most loved up spud muffin in Ireland.

Hot potato seeks wife

By SUN REPORTER

IT was crunch time for Mr Tayto yesterday as he tried to bag a crisp-looking wife.

And a feast of beauties including Karena Graham and Jenny Lee Masterson were vying for the hand of Ireland's most EDIBLE bachelor.

The tasty suitors chased Tayto through the streets of Dublin, kitted out in their wedding finery and wellies.

But Mr Tayto's wingman Simon Delaney said the lucky girl can't have a CHIP on her shoulder.

Simon joked: "She'll have to be a solid girl, beef to the heel type, you know?

"He loves a woman who looks good in a pair of wellies. But looks aren't everything — she'd want some brains too. I mean she'd definitely have to know the business end of a heifer."

An Open Letter to the People of Ireland.

As you all know, I have spent the past number of months searching for my own lovely girl, who might one day become Mrs. Tayto. Today, I'd like to announce that I have found her. In fact, I have found her many times over.

In the last few months I have met more beautiful, talented and interesting women than I have known my whole life. My little black book is overflowing with eligible ladies and my social life is a whirlwind of activity the length and breadth of the country. In fact, I'm having so much fun that I have come to the conclusion that I'm not yet ready to settle down.

Variety is, as they say, the spice of life and just like one day I might want cheese and onion and the next salt and vinegar, I don't think I can be just a one woman kind of guy. So, I have decided the bachelor's life is for me.

I hope I haven't broken any hearts and that none of you lovely ladies are too disappointed. In my search for love, I hope I have also spread a little.

Love,

Mr. Tayto

Mr. Tayto

MY SIX PACK

AH WHEN A FELLA GETS TO A CERTAIN AGE, HE BEGINS TO NOTICE THAT HE'S BECOME, LET'S SAY, A LITTLE FULLER IN FIGURE, THE BUTTONS MAY BE POPPIN' OFF THE JACKET, THAT SET OF CAR KEYS MIGHT BE A LITTLE MORE DIFFICULT TO WRENCH FREE FROM THE TROUSER POCKET.

I was always a great man for the walking, though it was only to and from the car, in and out of the lift and a stroll from my office to the canteen and back. But recently I've signed on the dotted line and sentenced myself to twelve months in the gym. Now, I have to be honest and say only part of the reason for me joining up is the fitness, the other is that I reckon it might be a good way of meeting a very fit lady. But what an eye opener the modern gym is. First of all the place looked liked it came right out of Star Wars, intimidating machines of shiny grey steel flying at high speed, up and down, in and out. Honestly, I was expecting an army of Stormtroopers to arrive any second and force me to do twenty push-ups there and then. I've tended to stay away from those push you –pull you contraptions and concentrate more on stuff like swimming and I do love the sauna and especially a good steam.

Then there's the classes, you know the ones; Tai Chi (whatever the hell that is?) Tums and Bums, (does what it says on the tin!) Spinning (sure me own Mother did that) Pilates (again, no idea!) Yoga (well that's just bending your legs to where they shouldn't go).

But I did give the Aerobics classes a go. Mainly because the instructor, Tania, is a fine looking thing indeed, in fact a vision wrapped in pink and orange Lyrca.

I thought I'd be a shoo in with her as I was the only male in the class and I felt she was giving me the eye as we were lining up for the session. "Yes Tania, I am flexible," I would answer, but the reality was, after five minutes of lunges I was ready for the ambulance. The sweat was rolling off me and I caught my reflection in the floor to ceiling mirror flailing about like a broken clothesline in a gale. My fellow Aerobicers were gradually moving further away from me until the entire class was huddled together behind the exercise mats. I didn't return for the following session, I think I did them a favour. I did however stick to my keeping fit pledge, I still do the swimming nearly every day, even freeze me spuds off with a Christmas Day charity swim in Bettystown.

I'm on the bike now too, I've even taken it for a spin inside the factory, the girls on sorting thought it was hilarious. But it's important to keep fit because your 'health is your wealth' as Granny Tayto used to say (or was that Chairman Mao?) No, I'll never be a Muscles from Brussels I'm happy to be a Spud from Dub!

LOTTO FEVER

IF I WAS TO SAY TO YOU, AN CRANNCHUR NÁISIÚNTA, HOW MANY OF YOU WOULD KNOW WHAT I WAS ON ABOUT?

But if I were to say 'Lotto' you'd all know! I remember the week the National Lottery started back in 1986. Things were difficult back then (how we've come full circle eh!) and suddenly everyone had a chance to be rich. The jackpots were £250,000 in old money back then, but sure you could have bought a house for fifty grand so it was the equivalent of a few million these days! I remember when a load of clever types thought they could work out how to cheat the system and play every combination ….ah it was Mission Impossible stuff! But believe it or not, they pulled it off, even though they had to share the jackpot so didn't make as much money as they thought. The Lottery added three more numbers to the game after that to make sure it wouldn't happen again.

Everyone knew someone who had won something, and lotto fever really took off in Ireland. The biggest ever unclaimed lotto prize of £2,713,334 was back in 2001; and guess where it was bought? Only Coolock! I remember everyone went mad - searching bins and pavements for discarded tickets. It was like a Willy Wonka golden ticket! There was only ninety days to collect the money so it expired in September of that year. It became the stuff of legend in Coolock, and I knew ten people who had all accidentally thrown away a ticket, and to this day, they always wondered did they have the winning numbers. Can you imagine it!!

During the boom years, a lot of people stopped playing the lotto believe it or not. The starting jackpot of just over a million, wasn't enough for folk anymore…not when bankers were suddenly earning million euro bonuses and people with ordinary jobs were driving around in hundred grand cars …if ever there was proof that we'd lost the run of ourselves! Even these days, it does make me laugh when people only play when there's a big rollover jackpot.

On an average week it's over 2 million euro! It's as if that's not worth playing for, but when it gets to eight million, ah sure we'll all have a flutter!

No one has ever been able to explain this logic to me. Of course now that we're in a recession, people will play any given Wednesday or Saturday if they've a couple of euro to spare. In fact, there's a number of Irish people who when asked about their retirement plans, they'll tell you "Ah sure I'm going to win the lottery".

Then there were the offshoots of the lottery. The Telly Bingo hosted by that gravely voice girl Shirley Temple Bar - there was something about that girl I could never quite put my finger on. Did anyone else think that?? Then there was Winning Streak, Monday Million and all the other lottery game shows; as a nation, we're still mad for the lotto. An American fella said to me once after a holiday here, that when he thinks of Irish people now, he thinks of them sitting down to a pint, with a bag of Tayto and a scratch card!

What about the Euromillions? Who'll ever forget when Limerick lass Delores McNamara picked up enough money to buy her own planet?! We've had a syndicate of twenty-eight people in the factory for the lottery and the Euromillions for years, but the most we ever won was €2,500. We were delighted, but once it was divided up, it was €89 each, not quite enough to retire on, but we had a good night out! Aside from that, I once got a box of chocolates on a Christmas scratch card so I've definitely spent more over the years than I've ever won, which is the same as most Irish people - but when we see the likes of Delores adding a third swimming pool to her house, we just keep playing. Next time it WILL be me!

The SPUD MAGUIRE

IT WAS GREAT BEING A GAA FAN BACK IN THE SIXTIES AND SEVENTIES, I REMEMBER ROCKING UP TO CROKER WITH MY PA AND GRANDPA AS A YOUNG LAD AND BEING HOISTED OVER THE TURNSTILE AND INTO THE ELECTRIC ATMOSPHERE FOR A FINAL.

In those tasty days the Dubs seemed to always make it into the final. As part of Heffo's army we roared our way through six finals in '74, '75, '76, '77, '78 and '79! I will never forget standing on a jam packed Hill 16 watching on as a blue jersey hoisted the Sam skyward and made all us Dubs feel invincible! Great days indeed!

Of course it didn't begin and end with a final, we'd spend our lives down in Parnell Park in Donnycarney cheering the boys on during the league, and when I was old enough me and the lads would dissect the games over a pint or three in The Goblet.

Nowadays, the game is ruled by the mighty Kerry and Tyrone, and it's been way too long since the Dubs have had a sniff of the Sam Maguire. Back in the days of obscenely tight shorts and long hair we had some magnificent players; the mighty Kevin Moran, Brian Mullens in midfield, the big lad Jimmy Keaveney up front and of course our greatest goalie, in this humble spuds opinion anyway, Paddy Cullen. Every time I hear his name I shudder as I remember the mashing Kerry gave us in 1978 when Mikey Sheehy lobbed Paddy.

Mind you, I shouldn't neglect to mention the Eighties either, as we were made proud once again and took home Sam in 1983 with the original 'The Rock', Barney Rock, laying down the law. Then of course the Nineties gave us some shining stars like Jason 'Jayo' Sherlock, a real ambassador for the game! Mind you like the rest of Dublin, I was in rag order in '91 after those four run ins with Meath only to lose after three drawn games. Nearly put me off moving the Tayto factory to Ashbourne!

It's been lean times since I was last in Croker in 1995, but my love for the game has never diminished and I'm sure one day, please God, I'll be back on the Hill with the best supporters in the world. The Hill doesn't have quite the same buzz when you're watching the back of Bono's head as he's singing 'The Streets Have No Name!'

HALF BAKED REALITY

NOT SO VERY LONG AGO – WELL, THOSE OF YOU OVER 30 MIGHT JUST REMEMBER IT – MOST OF IRELAND ONLY HAD TWO CHANNELS.

Now the average house has about two hundred! You'd think that with all those fancy channels to choose from, there'd be shedloads of telly worth watching. So how come every time I turn on the box these days, there's nothing on but reality television? Reality used to be about getting out and meeting people and the like, and TV was for entertainment and a bit of escapism. Years ago our idea of Reality TV was a good documentary, or perhaps Blind Date. Now between Big Brother, Every Country's Got Some Sort of Talent, You Are What You Eat/Wear/Date, Living Like An Animal, Living With an Animal, Shipwrecked, Seasick, Wife Swapping, Job Swapping, Who Wants to Be a Millionaire, Who Wants Money Off a Millionaire, I'm Heavier Than My House….where's it going to end? And of course, we've had our own stab at it. There's been shows on boats, celebrities in hotel, houses, restaurants and campsites, talent shows and model searches. I never thought I'd see the day that we swapped proper television for this. Sure they may as well just put the CCTV from your local shopping centre on for a few hours a day!

The talent shows I'm not so irri-tater-ed with. We've always had talent shows in Ireland. Who remembers Tops of the Towns! The problem with alot of them these days is, it's all about churning out boyband clones. Just look at JLS! That Louis Walsh has a lot to answer for!

I've been approached myself to do a bit of the old reality TV. I was asked to do Celebrities Gone Wild but they changed their minds when they realised I'd have an unfair advantage with the whole 'living outdoors' aspect, what with being a potato and all!

Then Celebrity You're a Star came knocking, and I have to say I was tempted! I always fancied myself as a bit of an entertainer, I'm the first up at the Tayto Christmas bash with a song! But then the crew in the factory admitted that just because I was first up, didn't mean I was any good, so I thought better of it.

It all got me thinking though, how about a reality show in a crisp factory? Now everyone would watch that! We could follow some of the legendary factory fillies at work, the drama, the fun, the spuds, the action.... Yes, I can see it now - how about The Crisp Factor, Ireland's Got Tayto, I'm a Potato Get Me Out Of Here, The Spud Life, You're aSpud, Peel or No Peel....the possibilities are endless! I see a new project on the horizon.......!

FRYING VISITS

I NEVER THOUGHT I'D BE SAYING THIS, BUT WHAT WOULD WE HAVE DONE WITHOUT MICHAEL O'LEARY?

Without him the majority of us would not have been able to have eight holidays abroad a year. You'd have to have saved for months to visit that friend in London, and taken out a bank loan for that cousin's wedding in Italy. Of course, the recession has put paid to a lot of that, but flying is still much cheaper than it was when I was growing up, and the four hour ferry to Holyhead was the only way to get to England!

Cheap flights may have made travel available to everyone, but it has also made flying the most awful experience since having verrucas burned off your feet as a kid. Ok, so we can't blame Ryanair for everything - all that extra security for example. After all, I don't think terrorists wait for weeks or months until there's a special offer on flights. But we can blame them for turning airports into the equivalent of the Clery's sale after Christmas.

Flying used to be such a civilised way of travelling. Now it's hordes of people jostling and pushing their way past you, bashing your ankles with over-loaded trolleys, trying to work out if their queue is moving faster then the one beside it. With Ryanair flights, seating isn't assigned, so there's no point in pushing your way to the front of the queue - you're not getting a better seat! But no one wants to waste a second queuing that could be spent shopping for over-priced things you don't really need in the non-duty free duty free, or having the first drink of the day at 9am at the departure gates. Ah isn't it great being able to drink 24 hours a day with no one tut-tutting? Because hey - you're on holidays!

If you thought things were bad at the check-in desks, just wait till you get to the departure gates. This is where things really turn nasty. First of all, the Ryanair gates are usually as far away as they can be whilst still being in the airport. It's like walking half the way home again. Then when you get there, it's like a riot in a bingo hall. Everyone keeps one eye on the monitors, and the second the gate is announced, it's a stampede. I was nearly a mashed potato one year when I tried to beat some enthusiastic Ryanair holidaymakers to the boarding queue. And who can forget Mr O'Leary's great invention - the priority queue. For just a few extra euro, you can feel like a VIP by....well just by being allowed stand in another queue that lets you and a third of all the other passengers get on the plane first. But then the first few rows are always kept till last, the emergency exit seats with their extra leg room, are assigned by the staff, so you're not going to get any special sort of seat by getting on the plane first. Ok, so you might get off the plane two minutes before someone in row 26, but that's not going to make that much of a difference to your holiday!

Surely when you're on the plane, you can finally sit back, relax and enjoy the flight? Not quite! With Ryanair Mr O'Leary never misses an opportunity to take a bit more money off you! When a paper jokingly said he was going to start charging for the loo, everyone believed it without question. An in-flight four day old sandwich will set you back a small fortune, you can now gamble mid-air with the Ryanair scratch cards, the alcohol comes in bags, and then you're politely asked to clean up after yourself. And there's no Tayto available on board! But at least after all of that, your holiday can begin. Except don't forget with Ryanair, they will drop you at least a hundred miles from where you thought you were going, and you'll have to get a bus the rest of the way!

Having said that, we'll all still keep flying with them, and maybe one day I might even see one of the Ryanair calendar girls on board! Now that would be worth a ten euro surcharge!

TAKE *on* DUBLIN

AS ANOTHER FAMOUS SON OF THE CAPITAL SAID - "I REMEMBER DUBLIN CITY IN THE RARE OUL' TIMES" MYSELF AND THE LADS REMEMBER ALL SORTS OF FACTS AND TRIVIA FROM BACK IN THE DAYS WHEN PEOPLES' HOBBIES WERE SITTING ON WALLS, HANGING AROUND, AND LIGHTING CANDLES FOR THE DEAD.

HERE ARE JUST A FEW BITS OF MY FAVOURITE DUBLIN BITS, BOBS AND TRIVIA FOR YOU!

Dubliners have a knack for giving charming nicknames to statues around the city - there's Molly Malone aka the 'Tart with the Cart' at the bottom of Grafton Street. The 'Hags with the Bags' by the 'Ha'Penny Bridge', the 'Flue with the View' in Smithfield and the 'Stick in the Sick' (the Spire!). Then there's the legend that was Phil Lynott outside Bruxelles - 'The Ace with the Bass', and colourful character Oscar Wilde, 'The Quare in the Square'. And I couldn't possibly forget grumpy old Paddy Kavanagh's bench on the Grand Canal known affectionately as 'The Crank on the Bank'! Then there are a couple which are no more - the 'Floozy in the Jacuzzi' which is now in a City Council lock-up somewhere and the 'Chime in the Slime', the Millennium Clock in the Liffey, which was about as reliable as a sundial in the dark and had to be removed four years before the year 2000. I was angling for a 'Spud in the Mud' statue in the Phoenix Park but it hasn't happened yet.

Buck Whaley was officially the first Dublin messer. He'd accept any bet going. The first was a bet he couldn't go to Jerusalem and back in 2 years, which he did and won £15,000. Then he was bet a tenner that he wouldn't jump out a window into a passing carriage and kiss its occupant. The next was to go to Paris and rescue Louis XVI from the guillotine.... sensibly, Buck turned this one down. Fittingly, there's now a nightclub named after him where a lot of messing still goes on today.

I wouldn't recommend you try testing some of these, but there are some weird laws in Dublin that still exist on paper since the old days. Such as:

In Trinity College students can demand a glass of wine at any time during an exam, provided they are carrying their sword.

If you are granted the freedom of Dublin city, you are allowed graze sheep in Stephens' Green.

It is illegal to smoke tobacco in Grafton Street!

Tallaght is one of the oldest towns in Dublin and means Plague Cemetery. Coyler's sister lives there and said it's still a bit like that on Saturday nights!

Back when I was a youngster, there was a cruel tradition amongst fellas. If you got stuck with a girl you didn't like, you'd arrange to meet her upstairs in Keogh's on Clanbrassil Street. But Keogh's was only one storey high!

Quinner's dad was told by his great granddad that O'Connell Street Bridge used to be made of rope and could only carry one man and a donkey. But nowadays it can hold a load of donkeys! According to most angry taxi drivers anyway.

How many pubs are there in Dublin? Any ideas? Over a thousand!

Did you know that The Late Late Show, broadcast live up in RTE in Dublin, is the longest running chat show in the world? Nearly everyone in the country must have been in the audience at this stage! A bit like the James Bond films, everyone has their favourite host. Gay Byrne is the Sean Connery, Pat Kenny the Roger Moore, and we may need a few more years to find out if Ryan Tubridy is the George Lazenby!

- Ross O'Carroll Kelly. If ever there was an opposite to a Humble Dub-Spud like me, it's Southside rugby jock Ross. Sure I don't understand what he's on about half the time, "the pen is Padraig", "a good set of top tens" and an "Allied Irish"? Am I just too old or too Northside??

- For a major city, Dublin must have some of the worst public transport in the world, outside of possibly Karachi. We have one train line which the Dart has to share with intercity trains; two metro lines that don't meet up; quality bus corridors that work as well as a chocolate teapot and if you want to drive into the city, by the time you've paid for parking and still been clamped, it'd be cheaper to just buy a new car!

BACK *of the* NET

LET'S FACE IT, THE IRISH ARE GREAT AT PRACTICALLY EVERYTHING, INCLUDING SOCCER.

We've had our fair share of incredible players over the years, the likes of Giles, Steve Heighway, Mick Martin and the legendary Don Givens. I've been a lifelong fan of the beautiful game and I was even at that famous match against the USSR when Don scored a hat trick against the Reds. Mind you if everyone who says they were at that match was really there, then there would have been three million crammed into Dalymount on that momentous day back in 1976. Then there was all those 'nearly years' when we were the Cinderellas of international soccer, until a Scotsman gave us our break and we were into the European Championships in 1988. And that's when the golden years of Jack Charlton kicked in. Big Jack is probably the most popular Englishman ever in Ireland. For the following years the Credit Unions were busy helping send Jackies' Army all around the world, and paying for oversized green hands, hammers and leprechaun hats.

I mean who doesn't remember where they were in June 1990 when our lads did us proud in Italy? The Italia 90 Team are still the only Irish team ever to meet Pope John Paul II. Rumour has it that Jack told the lads he'd packed enough Tayto for a pack each a day all the way to the final! Now there was an incentive to stay in the tournament if ever I heard one…of course it was only alleged but whatever it was that Jack did, it did the trick.

Me and the lads all went over to Italy for a fortnight – ah, it was one of the best trips I ever did! I remember the date well - June 25th, the match against Romania in Genoa and we had great tickets. We were on the edge of our seats during that penalty shoot out. When O'Leary put the fifth peno in the back of the net, it was magic, best feeling in the world! Olé olé olé olé!!!! We spent the next five days travelling down to Rome for the quarterfinal match against Italy, but we all know how that ended. Still, it really was one to tell the grandkids. Then of course came the Mick McCarthy years, and all the drama at Saipan, followed by my old buddy Kerr and then Staunton - great player, shocking manager. We'd all love to see an Irishman at the helm but it hasn't worked - it took an English fella to do it before, and these days we're trying an Italian, so maybe Trapattoni is the man to put the boys in green back on top! But no matter what, I'll always wear my green jersey with pride!

TAYTO
GOLDEN POTATO CRISPS
TAYTO
GOLDEN POTATO CRISPS
TAYTO
GOLDEN POTATO CRISPS
OPEL

I'VE AVOIDED BRINGING IT UP FOR AS LONG AS POSSIBLE - THE DREADED R WORD. (NO, NOT POTATO ROT; THINGS AREN'T THAT BAD). I MEAN THE RECESSION, THE BUST, THE CREDIT CRUNCH, THE SLIDE…CALL IT WHAT YOU WANT.

The Celtic Tiger ended as quickly as bursting a bag of crisps; and was equally devastating, (Dramatic? Me? Have you ever accidentally burst the last pack of crisps in the house after the shops have closed??). And all the wise guys like McWilliams, Hobbs and Lee got to say "we saw it coming", "what goes up must come down" and "it couldn't last forever". Jaysus, you'd swear they were talking about the circus coming to town rather than people's livelihoods! Now I'm not saying it wouldn't have happened if I'd been elected, but sure we'll never know now…

I'll tell you one thing; I'm damn glad I put all my money into potatoes rather than shares in the likes of Anglo or AIB whose shareholders' lifelong contributions to their pensions are worth less than a packet of Chipsticks! It's like Pa used to say, always keep a few bags of crisps in the back of the cupboard for a rainy day. And since we live in Ireland, there's always going to be a rainy day!

When you look at it now, in the cold light, we'd lost the run of ourselves and no-one was watching the shop; sub-prime this fellas with helicopters going down to the shops to pick up a pint of milk, new golf clubs appearing every weekend.

But the worst thing of all, was the queues of young people outside apartment blocks, having been told that if they didn't get on the property ladder right now, then they never would! They had their chequebooks, or very often their parents' chequebooks open, desperate to buy a gaff as the developers added zeros on like they were going out of fashion.

The banks were suddenly delighted to lend you ten times your salary, no questions asked. There were housing estates popping up in every field, a hundred miles away from the nearest school. 'Buy a house in Monastereven, only thirty minutes from Dublin city centre!' True, if you drive at 3am on a Sunday! And you'll be driving on a motorway that cost a billion euro and still isn't finished! That's what the 50 in M50 stands for - 50% there! Ah, it was shocking when you look back now, the ride that these young people were taken for.

There were a lot of us older types who could see what was going on, but as I said you didn't want to come over all moany, and if we're totally honest we all got caught up in the Celtic Tiger enthusiasm, it was infectious. Sure how could you not with tax at an all time low and jobs galore and the Teflon Taoiseach Bertie giving us all free money with the SSIAs. I mean, these were unprecedented times; the government actually giving us money! None of us will ever see that again in our lifetime!

So now the State is in a right state; the banks are writing off debts left right and centre, foreign investment pulling out of the country and jobs being shed all over the shop. We might be hurting, but one thing this entrepreneurial spud knows for sure; we'll never be beaten! As a Nation that's lived through the famine and all kinds of adversity, we'll undoubtedly pull through. And besides some good might actually come out of this recession. For one thing, it might put an end to some of the jumped-up nonsense that I've been noticing around the country over the last few years.

You see, not only did we lose the head when it came to our economic wealth, I think we lost our minds with some of the fads that came into this country along with the cash! I'm sure most of you are familiar with at least some of these:

BARS THAN AREN'T BARS

I say, good riddance to 'Nail bars', 'Juice bars', 'Sushi bars' and 'Oxygen bars', in fact anything that calls itself a 'bar' and doesn't sell Tayto crisps and pints!

FARMERS' MARKETS

What ever happened to real farmers markets? All of a sudden they were infested by Celtic Tiger tossers. And these so-called farmers started to appear selling stuff that never even touched a field. Truffle parfait anyone? Yer joking!

DOGS AS FASHION ACCESSORIES

Suddenly you were no one unless you had a Paris Hilton style small dog accessory. Preferably a pedigree that didn't clash with your outfit. It used to be, that if you wanted a dog, you'd go down to the ISPCA and give a needy mongrel a loving home. So good riddance to small dogs that cost more than small cars!

HOLIDAY HOMES

During the boom times it was no longer good enough to simply go abroad for a holiday, you were nobody unless you bought a holiday home! But thank God I didn't go all out and invest in a one-bed in Bulgaria, because since that low cost airline went bust, it now takes six days by camel to get there. Try and resell it, you couldn't give it away!

SUVS

It used to be that only some taxi drivers needed a seven-seater vehicle, but one of the strangest phenomena that occurred during the Celtic Tiger era was yummy mummies and their SUV, MPV or people movers (call 'em what ya like) obsession. I still can't figure out why they all thought they needed a 5-litre engine to drop their kids off at the crèche?

FANCY COFFEES

Until the year 2000, there were only two choices of a hot beverage in Ireland; tea or coffee. It was simple and that's the way we liked it. Then all of a sudden ordering a coffee became as complicated as understanding the booklet on the Lisbon Treaty. Moccachinos, Lattes, Grandes, Expressos, Macchiato. Was I the only one that thought a Frappacino was the new five-door from Hyundai? The only question I want to be asked when I'm ordering a coffee is "Do you want milk in it?"

MAGAZINES ABOUT MAGAZINES

Another annoying product of the times was the influx of specialist magazines. Rainforests were obliterated just so you could buy your monthly update on Patios. (And before you think I'm making that one up, there is a magazine called 'Patio'!) From 'Building your own Starship Enterprise' in forty-six monthly parts to magazines on cosmetic surgery, from dog grooming to 'What to do with your kids' magazines. So now you need a magazine to tell you how to have a bit of craic with your kids! It had gone mad!

NEW!
ORANGE MOCHA FRAPPUCCINO
JUST €10

WEDDING PLANNERS

There was a time you'd laugh at stuff like that in the movies, but during the boom times, even Irish weddings lost the plot. It used to be that the bride, her Ma and the bridesmaid would organise the whole bash. But that all went out the window and you were nobody unless you had a wedding planner, never mind a celebrity wedding planner with a fake French name, who would spend all your money sprinkling a bit of glitter on your table cloths and tying a few balloons to the chairs. And then there are the bands; it used to be a DJ or a fella from the local football club who could strum a tune and get a hooley going, but during the Tiger years you had to have a string quartet as the guests arrived and a band that had at least one chart hit in the past twenty years. People were spending stupid money on their weddings when all you really need for a good wedding is yer family and friends and the obligatory drunken Aunt and pervy Uncle to make your special day special!

COSMETIC SURGERY

We used to laugh at the Yanks with their expressionless faces, big chests, ski-slope noses, and botulism was a type of food poisoning. Now even your average local hairdresser will inject it into your face for you while you get your hair done.

PANDEMICS

It used to be the Irish would have to be on their last legs before they'd even see a doctor, and a farmer would deliver a calf then have a cheese sandwich without washing his hands. The boom years brought a shedload of hypochondria to our door. Everyone started spraying disinfectant everywhere for fear of SARS, Bird Flu, Foot and Mouth, Swine Flu….you name it, we started washing our hands for it! No, I'll be glad to see the back of a lot of that stuff and nonsense that came with our perceived wealth, and I for one will look forward to people getting back to being more real. Yummy Mummies trading in their SUVs and walking the kids to school. Parks filled with kids playing footie instead of playing X Box or roaming around shopping malls as if they lived in Los Angeles!

It might take a few more years than our patience would like, but I think that Ireland will come through this recession a better place. Bring on the years of the Celtic Tayto!

Iconic Tayto pack. Andy Warhol should have painted it.

A BAG *of* LAUGHS

I LOVE A GOOD JOKE AND I'M A HUGE FAN OF GOOD COMEDY SHOWS. ONE OF MY FAVORITE THINGS TO DO EVERY MAY, IS TO GIVE COYLER AND MICKO A SHOUT AND HEAD DOWN TO KILKENNY TO THE CAT LAUGHS FESTIVAL.

It's where the cream of Irish and international stand up comedy can be found plying their gags in every hotel, bar and backroom in the Marble City. The danger of course is that punters always think they could do better! Inspired by years of admiring comedians, Coyler had a go at telling a few gags at his brother Little Coyler's wedding, but he soon learned it's harder than it looks! It kicked off fairly well but then he started into the old 'mother in law is so fat' jokes, and then the next thing the bride bursts into tears, the double doors to the ballroom open and in strolls the mother of the bride, all twenty stone of her. Poor Coyler, he didn't even notice what was going on as the eejit was so nervous he just kept on going. I ended up pulling the microphone off him. Every time we go to a comedy gig now we ask Coyler if he still thinks he's funny! Cat Laughs is great 'cause we get to remind Coyler about it for three days solid - his sister in law still hasn't quite forgiven him.

There's something about being in a room with four hundred people laughing their socks off but then there's always someone in the audience who thinks they're funnier than the fella on stage; The Heckler. For instance, the comedian's up there in full flight when some eejit shouts up something like, "when's the comedian coming on?' The more experienced fellas will have a wicked comeback like, "now we know why some animals eat their own children!" or "when your Mother goes home!" pointing to the fella's girlfriend. They take no prisoners in the world of comedy. Which reminds me never, ever sit in the front row of a Jason Byrne Show! There I was minding my own business when he spots me out of the corner of his eye.

The next thing I know, the messer has hauled me out of my seat, stuck me in a cardboard box and dragged me around the stage in it for thirty minutes pretending I was The Pope in his Popemobile. I had to give members of the audience my blessing. PJ Gallagher the Naked Camera fella was there too, pretending to be the High Cross in the Phoenix Park! A pair of certifiable madsers! Which reminds me, the topic that got the biggest laughs at the festival this year? The recession! I know it's mad but I think every comedian we saw did a routine about it. Why are we laughing at such a disaster? I have a theory; because we're all in the same boat, we recognise that if you can't laugh about it all, it'll all end in tears! So rib tickle your way through the recession with a few of these:

What is the definition of optimism?
A banker ironing 5 shirts on a Sunday.

What's the capital of Ireland?
About 3 euro.

Whats the difference between a stockbroker and a pigeon? A pigeon can still lay a deposit on a BMW.

A concerned customer asked his financial advisor if the recession worried him. The advisor replied that he was sleeping like a baby. "Really??" replied the customer. "Absolutely," said the advisor, "I wake up in the middle of the night crying"

I lent my brother €50 last week. Turns out I'm now Ireland's third biggest lender.

My local Bank Manager said he was going to concentrate on big issues from now on. He'll be selling them outside the supermarket from Monday.

The FUTURE *is* POTATO SHAPED

PEOPLE HAVE BEEN ASKING NOW THAT I'VE FINISHED THE BOOK, WHAT I'M GOING TO DO NEXT? WELL LET'S JUST SAY THIS POTATO IS A HOT BED OF IDEAS.

I never stop thinking about new ways to feed my hungry customers, I've always got the next idea for a new snack or exciting flavour in my head to surprise and satisfy all you Tayto lovers out there. But aside from that, I have lots of other things up my red sleeve. Who knows, I could be the first potato in space? Spudnik! I might run for president? A potato in the Áras? What about a career in music? I could bring out a charity single; All You Need Are Spuds? Cheese Release Me? I might even open "TaytoWorld". I could be the Willy Wonka of the crisp world and show you all my Slicers, Dicers and Spicers. Now that sounds like a Mighty idea to me!

Or what about a film? Would anyone go and see a movie about me? Quinner said if there was one made, it wouldn't even go straight to DVD it would go straight to VHS! Thanks buddy, I can always rely on the lads to bring me back down to earth! But seriously, everyone the world over loves a great Irish story - The Field, The Commitments, Angela's Ashes, Darby O'Gill and the Little People. What if someone in Hollywood picked up this book and wanted to make a film about my life? Imagine that; a big-screen version of 'The Man Inside The Jacket'! Now that really would be something. Of course, I'm a hands on kind of guy, so I'd want to be involved every step of the way. I wonder who would play me, Mr. Tayto in his prime? I could always ask the Irish people for their thoughts, although I have a few of my own on that one, let me tell you. I know I don't exactly have movie star looks; in fact I've always seen myself as a

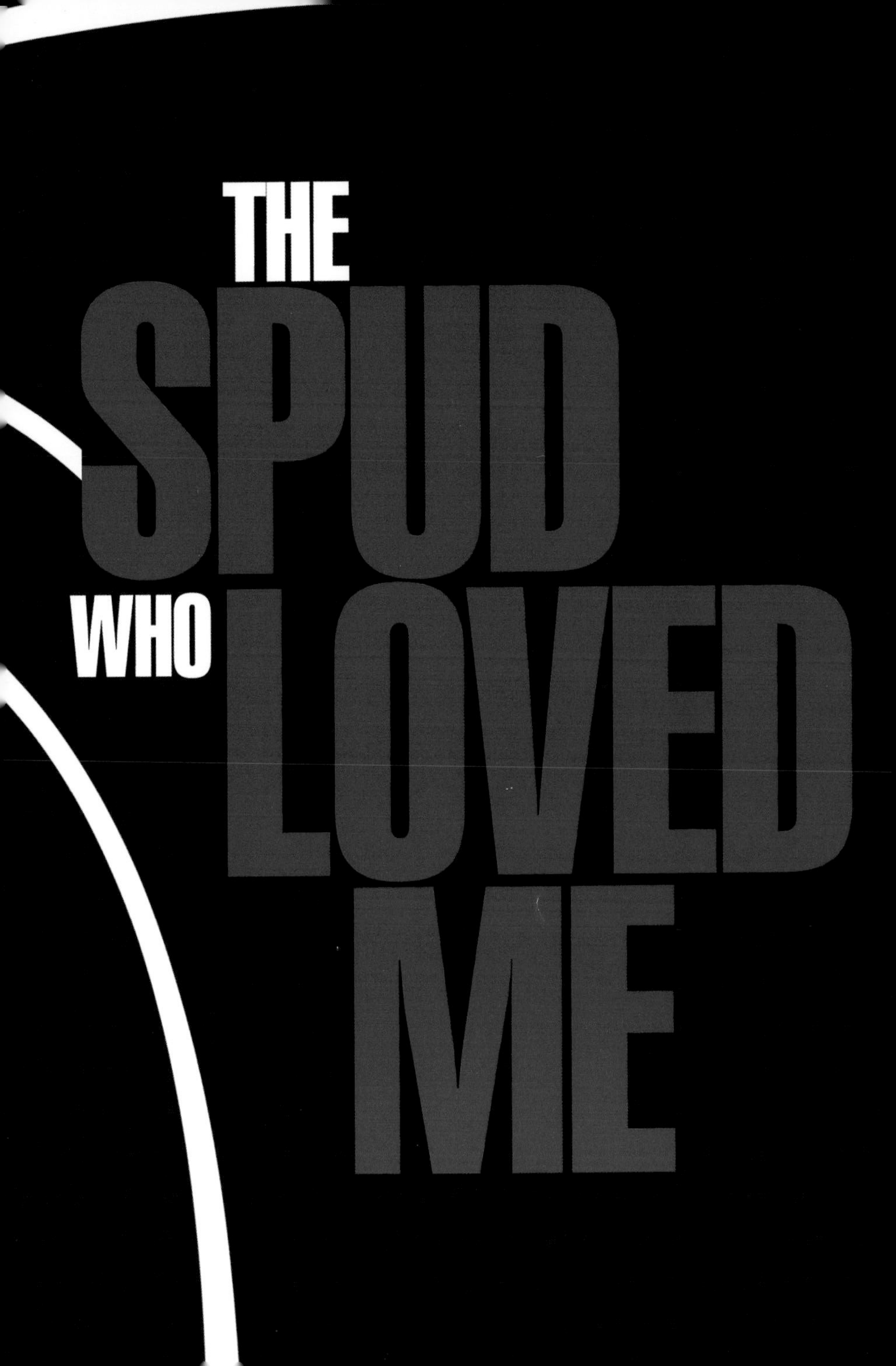
THE
SPUD
WHO
LOVED
ME

little bit rough around the edges but with that certain sex appeal, and of course a classic Irish good sense of humour. So I suppose someone like Gabriel Byrne might be a good choice and at least he could do my accent. There would be nothing worse than having some American eejit doing a 'top o'the mornin', version of a good strong Dub accent like mine. Who remembers Tom Cruise in Far and Away? "I've naw whish ta fight yah!" Nah, that would be a sellout!

Then of course, Colin Farrell would be the obvious choice to play the younger me and he has that maverick attitude that whoever might end up playing me would have to have. Oh, and by-the-way Coyler, if you're reading this, 'Danny DeVito' was not a helpful suggestion. I'll get you back ya messer! Just wait till you see who I'd get to play you if this ever happens!!

There would be a few things in the contract that I would need to make sure to draw a red line through. For instance; no revealing the secret recipes to my famous products. No one is aloud to burst into song; Tayto The Musical is not going to happen in my lifetime! And definitely no nude scenes!

Finally, there would have to be a car chase featuring my Tayto monster truck, where I save the day and get the girl by jumping the half open East Link Toll Bridge (still paying the toll of course, as I flew overhead shouting "keep the change sweetheart!") and drive off into the sunset! Now that would be an ending!

Well I have to say I've found the whole process of ploughing through my past to be one of the most satisfying things I've ever done. And I'm honoured - and a little surprised - that so many people want to read about a modest fella like myself. It's been a great journey, from those carefree school days with Coyler, Quinner, Micko and Doyler to taking over the running of the factory, entering the world of politics and on to those steamy love affairs. Digging out my old photos, diaries, and a few embarrassing stories I never thought I'd be telling anybody! I've given you my thoughts on everything from the recession to Ryanair, and from women to weather. And sure you probably disagree with half of it, but isn't that what makes the world go around!

It's been great to be able to dig up some old family history to share too - I feel like I've been on one of those Who Do You Think You Are? programmes - except if I had found any skeletons in my closet, I think I would have had to keep them quiet!

I want to say one thing for the record that I couldn't have done this without the love and support of the millions of Tayto fans out there. The good people who love the Original Irish Crisp and helped make Tayto a truly Irish icon and we can all be proud of that! In shops from Dingle to Donegal, if someone wants a packet of crisps they simply ask for 'Tayto'. The word has almost become the Irish for crisps and nothing else will do. Taytos are as Irish as the Irish themselves. In fact, I might apply to the powers that be to have it included in the dictionary!

So there you have it folks, my life so far, more twists and turns and ups and downs than the Roller Coaster at Funderland. But I'm glad to have shared the ride with you. Sharing is, after all, what it's all about, and that's what I hope I've done with this book; shared my story with my fans so that you all have a little more insight into 'The Man Inside The Jacket'. Who knows where I'll see you next – maybe The Oscars?!

The
END
For Now...